Mike Sargent was born in Ludlow and after education at The British School, 'Galdeford University' and Shrewbury Technical College became a bricklayer. A founder member of Ludlow Festival, he was stage manager for five seasons. He then spent five years in Greece, later returning to the UK where he resumed bricklaying and worked in a variety of other trades. After buying a Fedora he started writing poetry and prose. In 1998 his book, *My Old Man the Gasman*, was published in Ludlow. He was one of the first drivers for Shropdoc.

Also by Mike Sargent

MY OLD MAN THE GASMAN

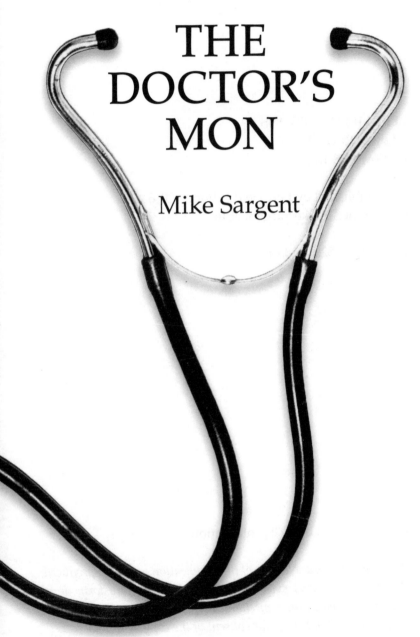

THE DOCTOR'S MON

Mike Sargent

LEFT FIELD EDITIONS
LUDLOW

LEFT FIELD EDITIONS
9 Lower Raven Lane
Ludlow SY8 1BL

First published by Left Field Editions 2016
Copyright © Mike Sargent 2016

ISBN 978 1 5262 0133 1

Printed in the UK by TJ International

Foreword

IN MARY WEBB'S NOVEL *Precious Bane* when Prue Sarn needs a doctor she sends first for the doctor's mon. He is the man who drives the pony and trap carrying the doctor and the apothecary's box full of remedies to those too ill to travel.

In the 21st century the out of hours doctor's service is in many ways similar. The sole object of the exercise being the delivery of a general practice GP to the patient outside normal working hours. It's just that the motorcar has replaced the pony and trap and mobile phones keep the doctor's driver and the dispatchers in contact one with the other. There are also printers and portable lap top computers in the car to contend with. All this gear complete with doctor will arrive generally speaking within three hours of a request for medical treatment.

It is a truly remarkable system and is completely free. Since even the unemployed, even those unable to support themselves are equipped with the very same electronic gadgets as are installed in the doctor's car or ambulance when the hand of God, or whatever 21st century mankind believes in, strikes them down with any kind of minor malady they expect an instant response. The chapters in this book are observations of this system of health care delivery.

All the characters are fictitious. Any person mentioned in any agency, institution or any organisation is wholly imaginary.

Mike Sargent
Ludlow 2016

1 The Boar

SUMMER, LATE EVENING. I am driving with Dr Gutsell through north Herefordshire and Stretford church is just 400 yards up a narrow lane.

Every time I pass this church I always think of Cosmas and Damian, the two saints to which Stretford church is dedicated.

In the very Harley Street of ancient Rome there is also a church dedicated to same twins. Other churches dedicated to them are in Jerusalem, Mesopotamia, Egypt, Constantinople and Athens.

They were Physicians and Surgeons. Known as the silverless doctors because they accepted no fees for their services. In AD 348 they removed the diseased leg from a Roman and then transplanted the leg from a black man, a dead Ethiopian gladiator. The operation is symbolised in Stretford church by the black and white candles, which represent the black and white legs.

Because it was the first limb transplant ever recorded, the opening page of the Fellowship of Surgeons shows the badge granted to the Fellowship by King Henry VII in 1492. Cosmas and Damian flank the crowned rose.

Twenty minutes later we arrive at our destination.

I remain in the car, watching Dr Gutsell pause and look at the door before knocking.

His eyes saw a thumb latch on a framed, ledged braced and battened door. The door was painted black. The door was as old as the house. An estate carpenter in the estate workshop would have made it from a tree felled on the estate. Two men would have cut it into planks. They would have used a sawpit. The one who pulled the shortest straw would have pulled the saw in the bottom of the pit. The sawdust would have dropped on his head. He would have worn a flat cap. After the wood had been seasoned the estate carpenter would have made the door for the new house.

Dr Gutsell held the handle and placed his thumb in the latch.

Throughout the life of the house every time the thumb latch was lifted, the door would have been the silent witness to all the entries and exits of man, wife, daughter and son.

And so I watched my doctor step into the lives of a family who already knew the destiny of the sick father.

I had driven through a rivulet of black stinking water to get to the house. This vein of greasy mud runs across the Bog into the Black Pool. The spring starts in the high trenches dug during the Civil War. The Bog was once meadowland but was stripped of its turf by Colonel Woodhouse to make fortifications for that war in 1650.

The widow who owned the land also had two horses and a spade taken, requisitioned, stolen, leaving her with no means to till her land.

With a billeted soldier and family to support, she starved.

War. Politicians love to go to war.

And now each side of the river of shit there is nothing.

Nothing except gorse has grown on the Bog since the Civil War.

The track to the house ended at the whitewashed wall of the privy and a chicken run. I wondered whether or not the The Bog had ever dried up. It should have done during the great drought in 1976.

I waited.

The day was sinking into the greyness of dusk and I decided to turn the car. I reversed and saw footprints made by pigs leading from a pigsty.

There was a new Ford Ka parked in front of the pigsty next to a 4x4 Nissan four door pickup.

The son's. The daughter's.

When I finished the manoeuvre I saw the garden.

There was a woman standing in the garden. She was wearing a low cut dress. She was looking at the garden. She was about 25 and started to pick peas. They were late, or no one had bothered to pick them. She split the pods and then removed the peas with her tongue. There were two rows of peas. They were all sticked with hazel sticks. Some of the plants still had white flowers on them. As the woman bent over to reach ripe pods I could see her shape and form. And there is hardly anything as beautiful as a female in a low cut dress picking peas and then removing them from their pods with her tongue.

I started to feel the delights of the voyeur.

I looked away and saw a small orchard. Half a dozen trees laden with small green apples. The far corner was overgrown, wild with neglect, fierce with thistles, and bristling with nettles.

I turned on the radio. Mozart. *Sonata number 21 for piano and violin.*

I looked for the woman shelling peas with her tongue.

Gone.

I reclined the seat. I started to construct an imaginary web of lives as they might have been for the family inside the house.

The father was an estate carpenter.

One daughter. One son.

Both left home.

I reclined the seat.

Lying back in position B, I saw the sky at the top of the windscreen move.

It was a slow movement.

I sat up, returned the seat to its original position. The car was moving. The handbrake was on. The car was lifting itself. It was starting to rock and roll.

There was nothing in the rear view mirror.

There was nothing in the left or right hand mirrors.

The car was rocking; it was rising and falling without human intervention.

Shit.

I was a little scared.

The car rocked.

I was more than a little scared. The Bog people. There were little people somewhere near the Bog. Or under the Bog.

They had been seen.

A cold sweat.

The dead from the Civil War.

I looked in the driver's mirror. I opened the door. Something was rubbing against the rear of the car. I walked to the back of the car.

And then, suddenly, I saw him.

I saw his broad back and the mud clayed to his side. He looked at me. He had teeth and tusks on each side of his lips.

He stopped his rubbing and he sniffed at me. He hunched his shoulders. His brown eyes bored into me, he saw me. And suddenly his mouth opened and he let out a roaring grunt and he took towards me and I backed away, but not fast enough. He held onto my trouser leg. He twisted himself and took a bite of material out of my trousers. I ran around the car. He came after me. I was moving around the car, the boar was moving after me. I looked behind, the beast was still coming. I managed to get back inside the car and I slammed the door on his snout.

The enraged creature roared.

I was inside.

He looked at the car.

His eyes were like bursting shells. He did not know what to do. I turned the radio up a few notches. His head moved to one side. He started to bang the car door with his head.

There would be a dent.

I turned the volume up a couple of notches.

I had no other weapon.

The boar lifted his ears.

The sound was having some kind of tonal influence on his brain.

The beast slowly turned and moved towards a gorse bush. I listened to the rustling of the plant as the boar retreated into one of his familiar haunts.

He did not like Mozart.

The sonata finished.

The gorse bush moved.

The boar's head appeared. Saliva dripped from the beast's lips. Sonata number 25 started. Arthur Grumiaux applied the bow to his violin.

The boar withdrew.

The animal did not like the sound of the violin.

He did not like Mozart.

I could still make out the clouds; they hid in their folds the last pockets of brightness.

I saw the doctor turn in the doorway. He was talking with the woman who had been shelling peas with her tongue. She was holding the 12-page guidebook, "What to do in the event of death."

The garden will never be dug again.

The father is gone.

The gardener is dead.

The son has a 4x4.

He won't dig the garden.

The daughter has a Ka.

She lives in a city.

"GET INTO THE CAR QUICKLY," I shouted to the doctor as soon as the woman closed the door.

He was not quick enough.

The boar came out of the gorse bush.

The doctor turned to see what it was.

"GET INTO THE CAR," I shouted.

The boar charged Dr Gutsell. He held his leather Gladstone

bag at arm's length pushing it into the face of the boar. The boar bit the Gladstone bag, holding it with his teeth. I got out of the car and kicked the boar's nearside back leg. The boar let go of the Gladstone bag and grunted.

Dr Gutsell saw the beast's tusks.

I saw the beast's tusks.

They were ivory white.

The boar liked the taste of the Gladstone bag so much he tried to take another bite out of it. Dr Gutsell ran across the Bog. The boar was in pursuit. Dr Gutsell was a fell runner and could therefore run. He could run faster than the boar. I followed the hunt. I lowered all the windows in the car and turned the volume right up. The car's headlights were on full beam, I was hitting the horn button and noticed that Gutsell could run at almost 20 miles an hour, faster than the boar, who turned and looked at me forcing me to stop. His eyes were phosphorescent. I thought that he was going to charge the car like a rhino.

I would have to fill in an accident form.

Boar charges car.

No one would believe it. Dr Gutsell would witness it.

Where was he? I could not see him. Where had the doctor gone? It was getting dark.

Where was he?

The boar was looking at the car.

He moved his head to one side.

He was listening.

He moved towards a gorse bush.

He did not like Mozart.

Dr Gutsell had run right to the very edge of the Bog. He was standing behind a five-bar gate. He was holding his leather bag. It was resting on the top bar of the gate. I flashed headlights at him. He climbed over the gate.

Once inside the car he asked me what kind of pig it was.

"That was a wild boar," I said.

"They are extinct," he said.

"Not in the Welsh Marches," I said.

"They are extinct, there's none left in Britain," he said.

"You just ran halfway across the Bog with one snapping at your heels," I said.

"It was a pig, a male pig," he said.

"That's a boar," I said, "and what's more he was wild."

2 He Fell Off His Tractor

BERT HILL'S SHORT WHEELBASE LAND ROVER with canvas top sounds like a tractor. This is because the exhaust pipe comes up through the nearside wing of the beast like an exhaust pipe on an old Ferguson tractor. There is even a little cap on the top of the exhaust pipe that closes when the engine stops running. This is to stop the rain entering the upright pipe. The reason Bertills' Land Rover has this type of exhaust is because he had a spare exhaust system on an old grey Ferguson parked out by the big Dutch barn guarded by a den of nettles. Bertills wasted nothing, he even bought stuff from sales that might 'come in' if it was cheap enough, as it were.

I heard Bertills' Land Rover pull up outside the rear door of our hospital. I watched Bert on the little TV screen trying to figure out how to open the door and I heard over the intercom someone else saying that you had to ring a bell.

I let Bertills in.

His sister was with him.

She is 10 years younger than Bertills but looks older.

She was holding his arm.

He was limping, badly.

"I nearly dropped jead," he said, "Damned if I didn't, bloody near thing."

"What's the problem?" I asked.

"Fell off me tractor," he said.

"He fell off his tractor," his sister said.

"Just sit there," I said, "I'll tell the nurse."

15

"He dunna want a nurse he wants a doctor," his sister said.

"It dunna matter who I sizz," he said.

"Could be broke," his sister said.

"It inna," Bertills said.

Big Sal was entering details from her last patient into the casualty computer. Nurses spend more time writing notes on cards and then duplicating them into a computer system with an electronic brain situated in a reinforced concrete basement 50 miles away, than they do nursing.

"Old Bert Hill's waiting, says he fell off his tractor," I said to Sal.

"Bet he's got his sister with him," Sal said, "she's like a parrot, repeats everything he says."

When I told Bertills that he would have to wait for about five minutes he asked where the toilet was.

"He goes every five minutes," his sister said.

"It inna that," Bertills said, "its just that I canna uld it like I used to, when I hasta go I gotta go and there ain't no messing about either."

I showed Bertills the toilet. Bertills went in and then resumed his waiting.

When Big Sal got him into the Casualty Bert rolled his trousers up. Big Sal saw a bruise.

"It goes from me knee right up me back," Bertills said.

"It goes right up and over his backside," his sister said.

When Big Sal pulled his trousers down she saw that his right hand buttock was all black and blue.

"What on earth have you done, Bert?" Big Sal asked.

"Slipped off the back of me tractor," Bertills said.

"He slipped off his tractor," his sister said.

Sal came into the room where the doctor and I were watching the television.

"Come and have a look at this bruise, I have never seen anything like it," she said.

The black bruise went all the way up Bert's leg from his knee and covered his right buttock.

"What happened?" asked the doctor.

"I slipped from the cab of me tractor and I fell right onto the side of the steel box which was lowered at the time on account of the fact that I'd thrown all bales out and slit 'em fer the ship," Bertills said. "Which was a pity because if the back box had ad a bin full then the bales uld 'ave broke me fall and I ud not have spent the night under the blinkin stars."

"Spent the night under the stars," his sister said.

"When did this happen?" the doctor asked.

"Yesterday evening just as it was gettin' dark," Bertills said.

"Yesterday," his sister said.

"I do not understand," the doctor said.

"It was half past five when it happened and I fell from me tractor and onto the back of the back loader and me backside caught the back of the box and me leg caught the side of the box and I could'na get up and I lay there all night and I managed to get up this morning," Bertills said.

"But it was minus seven last night," the doctor said.

"I dunna know about that," Bertills said, "could'na put a figure on it, well below freezing, it was kald."

The doctor was shaking his head.

Sal was shaking her head.

"I dunna know how he survived," his sister said.

"It was the dog and the knife," Bertills said.

"The dog or the knife, I don't understand," the doctor said.

Bertills looked at the doctor.

"First thing was when I was lying there on the bed of the steel box that there was still a bale left which I was going to bring back for the deep litter," Bertills said, "which was the most fortunate of things because it was getting kalder and kalder as I lay there and me back was kald and I lost me cap and then since I was lyin' on me side I felt me lambs-foot penknife in me pocket and so I rolled over and managed to get him out. Bob was standin' over me and he was lookin' at me, with his eyes and I looked back at him and he jumped over the side of the box and I wondered what he was doin' and then he jumped back uth me hat in his mouth. That animal is smarter than a human and my old Dad used ta say that dogs is more Christian than humans and he was right. He was fuckin' right."

"Language, Bert," his sister said.

"Sorry," Bertills said, "where was I?"

"The dog brought your hat," Big Sal said.

"I fergets things, yer know," Bertills said.

"You fergot ta turn the tractor off," his sister said.

"I never forgot to turn the tractor off," Bertills said, "why would I want to turn the tractor off when I was feeding the ship, yer silly uld quoice?"

"It ran all night," his sister said.

"I could'na turn it off, how did I know I was going to fall? If I'd know that I would'na have fallen would I!" and Bertills was almost shouting at his sister.

"He left it running all night," his sister said.

"Gordon Bennett," Bertills said.

"And so the dog brought your hat," the doctor said.

"And that's not all," Bertills said, "I was reachin' out towards the bale of hay and Bob was lookin' at me uth his eyes and I managed to sit up and catch 'old of the string and pull the bale towards me and cut it uth me knife and the bale burst and Bob started barkin' at the ship, he was keepin' um away, like 'cause I wanted that hay to cover meself. I just got the feelin' that I was goin' to be out all night. It was telepathic, me and uld Bob, cause he started to bring mouthfuls of hay towards me and that's how I covered me sen and then uld Bob cooched up beside me and all night I looked at the stars and every time the ship started to eat the hay Bob kept um away and then I saw dawn break and I was as stiff as a board but I could move and I struggled from under the hay and then it was kald, bloody kald and I remembered what me uld dad told me about hay and hay stacks and how they used to get hot in the middle and how he showed me how ta tell how warm they was ..."

"The doctor dunna want to know about that," Bert's sister said.

But Bertills kept on talking.

"... and what you does is to hammer an iron bar into the centre of the rick and leave it there and then when you pulls the bar back out after a good quarter of an hour if it sizzles when you spits on it then it's too hot...and that's how you takes the temperature of a hay rick, that's how it's done."

"The doctors dunna want to know about that," his sister said.

"I think that the best thing is that if Sal gets you onto the examination couch and then I'll give you a thorough examination," the doctor said.

"It's got tremendous possibilities, hay has," Bertillls said lying on the couch whilst looking at the fluorescent light. "Warm, I was as warm as toast under that hay, trouble is it makes yer scratch."

Bertills' sister sneezed. Sal supplied a Kleenex. Bertills' sister wiped her nose. The doctor ran his hands up Bertills' thigh. The doctor moved Bertills over and felt his backside. The doctor asked Bertills to lift his leg. The doctor could not find anything wrong with Bertills, excepting the massive bruise, he was almost normal.

"It would do no harm to have an X-ray," the doctor said.

"Now?" Bertills asked.

"Tomorrow morning," the doctor said.

"Not tomorrow, got the cows ta milk," Bertills said.

"He got his cows to milk," his sister said.

"I can't understand how you survived," the doctor said.

"The dog, three-point border collie, best dog in the world," Bertills said, "sold one of her pups to an American cousin, ship, they got a lotta ship out there."

"You should get a mobile phone," the doctor said.

"He's got one," his sister said.

"Bought a suit in Bridgnorth 10 years ago in order to go to old Bill Evans' funeral and the mon gave us one, part of the deal, a free phone and I never wanted one, but I had to have it," Bertills said.

"A phone," the doctor said.

"Ah, black un, but there was a catch," Bertills said, "You had ta put money in it and any road up they don't work on the side of the Bonk, it's the Dhustone, granite, dunna like the wireless."

The doctor laughed.

Big Sal laughed.

We heard Bertills leave.

"The exhaust is from a Ferguson tractor," I said.

The doctor did not know what a Ferguson tractor was.

"He was lucky," the doctor said.

"They are hard up on the hill," I said, "those on the side of the Titterstone are so hard that they have to take them out the back and shoot 'em like old dogs, cause they won't die."

The doctor laughed.

The doctor changed channels.

We watched *Newsnight*.

Paxman was telling the country that four soldiers had been killed by the Taliban and that personal borrowing had topped three trillion.

3   *The Mad Dog*

AT FIRST I THOUGHT it was a mobile phone, I thought it was some kind of new chime or some such thing like Beethoven's Fifth, for example, but all it did was to go beep, beep, beep and there were long pauses between the beeps and when the doctor went into the other room the beeps did not move with her and anyway Dr Green is not the kind of doctor who would attach strange chimes to her mobile. No, the beeps remained in the room, and there was another thing, there was a chair preventing the door from closing which was not normal because that was how we used to keep the door open before Sister Jones had the red box fitted on the bottom of the door.

The penny was beginning to drop.

The red box on the bottom of the door has a little lever which one can press down with one's foot in order to keep the door permanently open because the door to our consulting room is fitted with an hydraulic pump, designed to keep the door closed. All doors in our hospital have these devices because they are fire doors, they will keep back a fire for 14 minutes, after that time you will fry. But there are times when it is desirable to keep the door open permanently especially if you want to be aware of what's going on out in the corridor or if you want whoever is out there to know that there is someone else in the hospital as well as the single nurse in MIU.

All this is very important owing to the fact that more than 10 percent of the population are or have been on a journey into a supernatural realm or are lost on the edge of a parallel universe after having ingested plants or chemicals of a hallucinatory nature without the help or guidance of a Shaman.

So Sister Jones had the red box fitted, at great expense because the red box has a brain that is sensitive to heat and will close the door if necessary and thus allow the door to resume its original function as a fire door.

Getting down on my hands and knees, I was nearer to the bleeps, I also observed a little red light flashing and there were two little screws with Philips heads, which meant that inside was a battery.

The power to the brain.

It is not my job to maintain devices on doors but it was the only way to end the bleeps.

I pondered the reason as to why the device had remained the way I had found it and why doctors who had been using the consulting room all day had put up with it and came to the conclusion that the fact that doctors have a doctorate enables them to block out or suppress bleeps.

My penknife would not turn the screws.

I went to see Big Sal, the MIU nurse.

Inside Minor Injuries she has all kinds of devices for removing foreign objects from the human anatomy. She has electric grinders for removing plaster from legs, strange-looking forceps for removing glass from wounds, pliers for pulling out nails, saws, hammers, mallets, wire cutters, many different-sized needles and threads for sewing together skin, in fact the MIU has as many tools as a carpenter's shop, which was why ship's surgeons and carpenters worked closely together when doing amputations in the old days.

I borrowed a Philips screwdriver.

I removed the little panel. I replaced the batteries with new ones from our supply. The bleeps ceased. The red box was able to do its job again.

Happiness. Coffee.

Whilst we were sipping our coffee the printer started to make the about-to-print sound, which meant that 28 miles away in the call centre the dispatcher had sent a message.

The message was coming to me via the ether because mankind has found a way of vaporizing writing and sending it by means of levitation in defiance of gravity in a southerly direction until it unloads itself into our computer's hard drive, appears on the contraption's screen, prints and becomes a call sheet.

Think about it.

Greece 850 BC and a messenger ran 26 miles 385 yards from Marathon to Athens bringing the news of the victory over the Persians in less than three hours.

Now, 2,850 years after the famous courier dropped dead from exhaustion as he handed over his message in Athens, we magic a message. We can send one without sweat anywhere on the planet in less than one second!

Not only that but today thousands suffer a self inflicted torture after putting on expensive skintight running suits, with headphones in order to numb the brain which is so addled that they clutch silly little weights in their hands and then they happily train five or six times a week in traffic fumes before running marathons two or three times a year without carrying any sort of message, just for the fun of it, some even dying of exhaustion whilst clutching plastic bottles of water and Mars bars.

We are indeed a master race!

And it's almost run.

The call sheet is an important document, without it there is nothing. With it you have the address, the phone number, the postcode, the OS map reference and a description of the symptoms regarding the illness.

I looked at the call, it was routine and the address was on the other side of The Bonk.

Willow Cottage.

I did not know where Willow Cottage was.

It is better to call the patient before leaving because the Bonk or Titterstone is made of hard rock called Dhustone which has a strange effect on radio waves, sometimes it kills them, especially those used by mobile phones, it tortures them leaving pockets of dead areas.

Not only that but right on the top of the mountain facing east, towards the U.S.S.R., are the remains of an early warning system which during the Cold War was meant to listen in to radio communications from intercontinental rocket silos in Siberia thus giving our leaders 15 minutes warning of a nuclear attack which would allow them to disappear into underground shelters whilst the rest of the population fried like cod in a fish and chip shop.

The brains behind the early warning system however did not know that half a dozen ley lines cross the summit of a mountain in south Shropshire. Had they bothered to look at the ancient Mappa Mundi only 22 miles away in Hereford Cathedral they would have seen that the only hills on the first map of the world are the Titterstone Clees, this fact should have given them an inclination that perhaps such a holy summit was a dangerous place to put masts capable of listening right into the ether above Siberian rocket stations.

What happened was this: the electric kettle in the kitchen of the Craven Arms public house in the Titterstone Quarry started to broadcast conversations from the Kremlin in Moscow, which meant that the population of Clee Hill village would have known at least 30 minutes before our leaders when the world was about to blow up!

From that day to this the Craven Arms pub has been known as 'The Kremlin'.

It is advisable to therefore ascertain by means of a landline telephone any location on or near the Dhustone or 'God's stone'.

There was no reply.

My doctor looked at the call sheet.

Chest pain.

24

Indigestion?

Heart attack?

"Perhaps he's collapsed," my doctor said.

Since my doctor is from the Highlands of Scotland as well as having ginger hair she sometimes adds flurries of a Highland nature to her words.

"Could be kicking like an upside down tortoise," I said.

I had a vision of a man lying on the floor reaching for the telephone, waiting for help.

The situation was changing; the call had turned into another category.

It was now urgent.

As we moved in an easterly direction my doctor held one of the mobile phones in her right hand to her left ear, van drivers hold phones in the same manner as they swerve across double white lines.

"There is still no response," she said.

Since I was watching a sheep drag itself across the road still wearing last year's fleece because it had hidden in an old quarry during the shearing season I made no reply.

We were on the high road where you can see the yellow glow in the sky above Wolverhampton. It is an illumination of the night sky, which signifies the very beginning of the Black Country and the end of civilisation to a countryman, when a gust of wind almost blew our car across the road.

"The wind is strong up here," my doctor said.

"This is where the four winds meet," I replied.

"Is that Bridgnorth over there?" she asked.

"No," I replied, "Wolverhampton. During the last war people used to come up here on push bikes to see the Germans bomb it. It was said that the sky was so bright, the birds used to sing the dawn chorus."

My doctor laughed.

"Is that true?" she said.

"That's what the old generation used to say."

When we got to a cluster of houses where the O/S

coordinates said the address was we started to look with high-powered torches for 'Willow Bank'.

If 50 years ago you had driven a car through a village searching for the name of a house with one high-powered torch never mind about two the whole population would have been out to see what was going on, but that was before the human mind had been rendered insensible by cathode ray tubes.

We failed to find 'Willow Bank'.

We stopped outside a house with an outside light on.

The woman who came to the door did not know where 'Willow Bank' was, but she told me to go around the back to where her father was who was 80 and likely to give directions.

Out the back was an old brick barn that had been turned into a double garage with a pair of up and over doors, at the side, an open door led into a workshop smelling of leather.

Inside the daughter's father was trying to apply some kind of glue into a crack on a pair of ladies' shoes.

"Just checking ta see if this new fangled glue's any use, shoes today are useless, conna' repair um, what der yer want?" he said, looking straight at me.

The old man looked as fit as a fiddle, just his cheeks sagged a little as he asked what I wanted. When I told him he apologised because he did not know who lived up on the side of the Bonk, but that the house once belonged to a sett maker who died when he was 98 and had made the setts for Scunthorpe.

"Uld age got him in the end," he said, "lucky, hard bastards up there, used to have to take them out the back and shoot them like a dog, hard buggers just woodna die on their own ... dunna breed um like they used ta ... here you'll have ta walk at least a quarter a mile once you goes though the five-barred gate, which you can miss if you don't look but all you gotta bear in mind is that there's a track opposite which is a crossroads, like, a bridle path it crosses the road, see, it was the road used to carry coal on donkeys from the mine to the Castle. Ludlow Castle was coal-fired right back in the Middle Ages and there used to be 49 steps up to the house."

"Many thanks," I said, "and a happy new year, but I'd best go," I said.

As I walked back to the car I wished that I could have spent more time with the old man. I left him without even knowing his name.

I took his directions and turned right, went up to a T-junction, turned left and then went down a hill and then up a steep hill with banks each side which gave the impression of going through a railway tunnel because the trees each side touched and the wet tracks told that the road never saw the sun and the old man had told me that the five-barred gate was just half a mile on the left after the steep hill but we drove what seemed like a mile and came to a house right on the side of the road which said in white letters that it was called 'Shangri la'.

There was a figure standing in the porch of 'Shangri la'. He was holding a torch and wearing a white woollen hat almost pulled over his eyes. I stopped, got out, walked around the front of the car and asked the figure if he knew where 'Willow Bank' was. He did not, but said that he would ask his wife.

We watched two figures talking in front of a monster TV screen. It took a long time and they appeared to be arguing. When the man came out he said that it was a quarter of a mile up the road on the left and that the gate was set back from the road and that we could miss it if we were not careful.

As I drove up the road my doctor pointed the powerful torch out of the open window. She liked shining the torch. She liked the searchlight beam effect.

Whilst driving I pondered and came to the conclusion that anyone who did not know their neighbour was strange and that the man in the woolly hat, that looked like a tea cosy probably did not even know where he was living and that he wore a white woollen tea cosy on his head to prevent complete amnesia caused by rays from the plasma TV screen.

The gate was set back 100 yards from the road. There was a sign indicating that a bridle path crossed the tarmac road, but there was nothing to say that the place was called 'Willow Bank'.

My doctor illuminated our intended route and I noted the deep ruts.

We drove through the gate, leaving it open.

The track twisted and we came to a parking space with a two-berth caravan parked beneath a pair of beech trees. The caravan was once white but was now green because it was covered in some kind of moss. At the side of the caravan was an old Austin Cambridge saloon. It was dead and was covered in the kind of brambles Brer Rabbit hid in. On the right side of the track was the sign we had been looking for, 'Willow Bank'.

The track climbed and it got steeper and the ruts were getting deeper and I was waiting for the thump because I knew that soon the underside of our car would drag and I was going very carefully in order to minimize the damage because I knew we'd never get up the hill.

Our car is a Subaru Forester. It is a beast made in Japan by Fuji Heavy Industries. It has permanent 4-wheel drive. The boxer engine is a copy of the one used in Alfa Romeo sports cars. It sits inline with the transmission, instead of being offset, as in other FWD vehicles, this gives the animal a very balanced feel as well as a low centre of gravity. It has a chassis based on that of the Impreza, the famous rally car.

When our car finally beached itself the expected thump was an almighty crack.

I looked at my doctor who was shining the torch and hanging on to the little handle above her door.

"It's only the sump," I said.

"Oh, do you think it's broken?" she asked as she pointed the torch towards the earth.

"If it is then the ruts will be full of oil, hot oil," I said and the doctor got out with her bright light and started shining it under the car.

"I can't see anything," she shouted.

"Shit," I shouted, "get back in the car, I'm going to try to reverse."

"I'll shine the light," she shouted.

"You'll get covered in shite, get back in the car," I shouted.

Had doctor Jane Green's life moved in a certain direction then she could have been an actress or a model instead she used her brain, and became a GP, with long beautiful legs. I watched her get into the car and saw that her feet were covered in mud. She was wearing the wrong shoes; in fact we were both wearing the wrong shoes.

The car was stuck.

I turned the steering wheel, making the front wheels twist until they touched the sides of the ruts. The movement of each piston in a boxer engine is exactly countered by the corresponding movement of the opposite piston. I know this because I owned two BMW motorbikes.

Boxers do not vibrate.

When the engine under the bonnet of the Forester hit the red line we did not feel it, however we heard the mud hitting the underside of the chassis and we saw mud spraying up from the wheels as the front tyres gripped the sides of the ruts and the car twisted as it tried to escape and Dr Green was hanging on like grim death as we moved backwards sliding a little for almost 50 yards until I applied the handbrake whilst at the same time placing the gear lever into first and turning off the engine.

"We have to walk," I said.

"I have the wrong shoes on," she said.

"So do I," I said.

In Huntington there is a Museum devoted to Oliver Cromwell. He came from there. There is in that Museum an apothecary's box. It is a beautiful wooden box with little drawers containing all the drugs the apothecary needed in order to prescribe and prepare for the great man should he fall ill whilst slaughtering Irish Catholics.

Our box is not made of wood. It has little plastic drawers. It is not as big as the apothecary's box and probably not as heavy but heavy enough to carry up a muddy hill.

My doctor carried her Gladstone bag in her left hand and the torch in her right hand.

It is a rare thing to be anywhere on the planet without some kind of streetlight. It was a pity there was not a clear sky above us, I wanted to see how the stars looked, but just as soon as we left the sight of the car the wind decided to blow and all the leaves still hanging seemed to fall from the trees at the same time.

At the very same time I was thinking about stars Dr Green started to shine her torch in all directions because her arm was going round like a windmill.

I shone my torch at her and saw that she had one leg in the left hand rut and was trying to prevent the other leg from going into the right hand rut. She was trying to prevent herself from doing the splits. Unfortunately the more she tried the more her legs moved apart.

I did not know how to grab her.

Instinct told me to prevent her falling on her face, I held her in some kind of embrace, and her smell was the personal smell only her husband or lover would smell, it came out of her mouth in deep breaths. As I held her, her legs were trying to grip the slippery wet leaf surface and her hand holding her torch was also moving!

Her torch hit me right in the centre of my private parts.

The pain in each ball was individual and together.

"JESUS H CHRIST," I shouted.

"I'm so sorry," she said.

"Never mind about that," I said still holding her, "just don't fall over because we'll never get up."

Both torch beams shone into the trees and Dr Green was

on her knees, her leather Gladstone bag was somewhere in one of the ruts, I was sitting on my arse which had compressed the wet leaves to such an extent that the liquid had transferred itself through the seat of my pants and into my underwear.

"You have to let go of me," I said.

Eventually we both managed to stand but she had lost her Gladstone bag.

I found her Gladstone bag containing her stethoscope but could not find the drug bag.

After shining the torch up and down the left rut I saw it.

We continued climbing up the hill, moving in a zigzag fashion in order to make the climb less steep. I was now carrying the drug bag in my left hand with the torch tucked under my armpit so that on occasion I could take the doctor's hand should she need it on account of the inadequate traction afforded by her shoes.

Eventually we arrived at a point where the track turned sharp left and we were in a levelled yard surrounded by larch trees. We saw an Austin Champ Jeep parked next to two Morris 1000 Traveller estate cars suffering from a profound attack of both tin and woodworm.

Everything was covered in yellow pine needles, which were now falling like a fine mist because of the wind.

We could not see a house or anywhere a human could reside.

"Onward," I shouted.

The track became steeper.

I did not have to ask my doctor what was causing the dull pain in my private parts but as I struggled up the hill I noticed that I no longer suffered from sciatica, which was some kind of miracle.

Eventually and all of a sudden my doctor shouted "There it is," and she shone her light towards a house perched right up on the side of the hill and I searched with my torch and two beams found the steep steps.

"I'll count them," I shouted.

"There are only 29," I said taking very deep breaths.

"Thirty," my doctor said.

"That depends where you started from," I said.

We were standing on a new wood patio, it surrounded the old house and the new extension which was bigger than the original house. The surface was damp and slippery especially where the pine needles had fallen.

We heard the dog barking before we saw it.

The animal was in the house behind patio doors.

We could see a television flickering.

It was a grey beast, bigger than an Irish wolfhound.

When I pressed my face towards the window so that I might see better inside the house the dog jumped towards me scraping his claws on the window, giving me a close up view of his teeth.

He was not wearing dentures.

Dr Green and I looked at the animal.

"Entertain it," I said, "I'm going round the back to make sure there's no way the thing can get out, like a dog flap, or something and even if the doors are unlocked I'm not going in unless there's someone who can control the beast."

"All the time you were away it just watched me," Dr Green said, when I arrived back.

I looked at the great black dog looking at us through the glass.

"I thought it was grey," I said.

"I never noticed," my doctor said.

"It looks like the mad dog of Hergest," I said.

"The hound of the Baskervilles," my doctor said.

"One and the same," I said.

"Sir Arthur Conan Doyle," my doctor said.

"We are not going in there unless there is someone else in there and I don't mean a body lying on the floor either," I said, and the dog lifted his lips, and we saw spittle drip and I said, "I'm sure that that dog was grey when I saw it first."

"Probably the light from the television," my doctor said.

"Right," I said and I saw that Dr Green was holding her cell phone in her right hand.

"There no signal," she said.

"It's the Dhustone," I said.

"Thought I'd ring the number," she said.

"And then we'll see if Bonzo can answer a phone," I said.

Dr Green looked at me and I looked back at her and the hound watched both of us one at a time through the patio door with its tongue hanging out.

We had to go back to the car.

There was a signal on the phone in the car, only two bars, but enough.

The phone in the house was engaged, which meant it was off the hook which gave every indication that it was more than likely that whoever had lifted the device off the hook was on the floor, sunny side up, collapsed.

"I'll phone the police," Dr Green said.

"Make sure we get a dog handler," I said, "tell them to bring one of those things with a noose on the end or better still a shotgun!"

And so we looked in our folders for the phone numbers and found that the only way to contact the local policeman is by phoning 999, which is a call centre in the middle of Chester or some such place and that the call operator with the high tech thing in her ear is the most efficient, cut glass creature in the world and very happy when we gave her the O/S map reference.

Illuminated by the interior light we looked at each other and I wondered what it would be like to fall in love with a female of the species who is also a doctor and who would know about every bone and muscle in the human body and how it worked and how to get the best out of it and I imagined that two doctors going 'at it' would make the planet shake ...

"We are going to have a long night," Dr Green said.

"It will be as bad as a section," I said, "It'll be like waiting for the psychiatrist, the social worker and all the other buggers and all I want to do is to get home at midnight, finger the butt of a glass containing a dose of Scotch thereby placing myself under the influence of alcohol until my mind and muscles become impaired – and the ambulance."

"Good thinking," Dr Green said, "I almost forgot the ambulance, I'll phone and then it'll be here waiting when the police get here."

"And then they can load him into the back ASAP," I said.

It was not as difficult to ring the ambulance and what was more the operator was very much on the ball, so much so that she knew where we were, she knew that the drive was impossible to drive up and that the gate was back from the road and she gave the patient's name, which was a miracle and then she told us that the patient had been taken to hospital two hours earlier!

Dr Green looked at me and I looked at Dr Green and I wondered whether or not she was about to throw some kind of fit.

I waited.

What was going to happen next?

You never know what a Highlander will do.

Her face was swelling.

Especially one with ginger hair.

Her jaw was tense.

It was an explosion.

"Do you want me to throw the mobile phones out of the window?" she asked in anger, "we have three phones in this car, there are three phones back in the hospital, six dispatchers, God knows what kind of technology they use in NHS direct, we have climbed a mountain, seen the hound of the Baskervilles, I might just as well throw the fucking lot out of the window!"

She was shouting with a very strong Scottish accent added to each word.

"Don't throw the toys out of the pram until we have phoned the fucking police," I shouted.

"We have already phoned the fucking police," she shouted.

"Shit, I never used to swear until I worked with you," she shouted at me. As if it was my fault.

"We have to cancel them," I said lowering the volume.

"Who?" she said, calming down.

"The police," I said.

It is much easier to make a 999 call than to cancel one.

There is no way into the system that allows you to discuss the call you have made originally. What you have to do is to make another 999 call, wait until the dispatcher enters it into her computer, which will in turn talk to other computers in other call centres because in all probability the second call you make will not go to the same call centre and it will not be until the person looking at the screen sees some kind of flashing curser which gives some kind of warning, so that the system is alerted to the fact that it now has two calls to the same address!

You can in fact hear the pause, which the person makes who is operating the system. It talks to itself and as you wait you realise that eventually there will be no humans involved in decision making. Just machines fifty feet under the ground, protected from terrorists, which will monitor the end of the world, as we know it.

Which is almost as bad as the Cold War, when the Kremlin pub had all the information half an hour before anyone else.

The voice coming into our car, through the hands free system told us that a man had jumped off Ludford Bridge and into the river Teme and that helicopters and dogs were searching which meant that there would have been at least a two-hour wait before officers could have got to us anyway and would we confirm that we required a cancellation.

As we started to descend Angel Bank I asked Dr Green if she knew that during the Middle Ages coal fires heated our castle.

"I don't really care," she replied.

"This is the sort of situation that could drive a person to drink," I said.

"A good malt," my doctor said.

"Blair Atholl," I said.

"It was Blair Atholl malt whisky that put fire into the bellies of the Highlanders at the battle of Killiecrankie," my doctor said, her Scottish accent adding more and deeper flurries to each word as she spoke.

"That moved the Sassenachs from the pass," I said.

"Aye," she said.

Much speech leads to silence.

We held onto that void all the way down the hill.

When we got back to base I observed that the porter had been called in to remove a body to the mortuary, which was perfect. I would be able to replace the battery I'd installed in the red box on the door.

"You should not have done that," he said.

"Why not?" I said.

"The electrician," he said.

"What der yer mean?" I said.

"It's an electrician's job to replace batteries," he said.

"I don't believe it," I said.

"Mus'ent touch anything electrical, electrician's job," he said.

"But there ain't one," I said.

"Shrewsbury, there's one on call out," he said.

"Yes but," I said.

"That's how it is, electrician does anything electrical," he said.

"Even changing a light bulb?" I said.

"Can't do that, have to have ladder training for that," he said, as he started to close the door to the mortuary.

It was cold and getting colder and the hospital car park was lit by artificial light and I started talking to myself and shaking my head as I walked back towards the side door.

As I pushed the buttons on the combination lock the porter came around the corner pushing his trolley. The wheels on the trolley were larger versions of those on a supermarket trolley. What was more the front wheel was jammed so that there was a crippled mimicry of a tramp pushing a Tesco trolley up a hill with the brake on.

The trolley moved through the other entrance into that part of the hospital where the wards are and then a handful of dead leaves moved around the car park in a circular movement until they settled down and the car park returned to that state we call silence.

I entered the hospital.

Coffee.

4   The Long House

MY DOCTOR IS SEEING A PATIENT. The patient lives in a long house. A long house is a house with a barn attached. The original long house consisted of a single big hall with a fireplace in the middle where humans and their cattle lived together under one roof.

This type of house was common in Saxon times.

The man inside the house would consider himself to be more Welsh than Saxon; nevertheless he lives in a long house.

I am inside a car made in Japan. Japan is a country on the other side of the world. It is so far away that it is daylight there. Here it is early evening. The lights on the dashboard of my car are all illuminated. The lights are not small bulbs; they are made of some kind of plastic substance. When electricity is passed through it the substance becomes illuminated like a glow-worm's arse. There are dozens of glowing lights in front of me. It is a pleasing sight. It is right out of the 21st C. I could be the pilot of an aeroplane. I could be the pilot of a helicopter. I could be in a space ship.

That is the whole idea.

The idea is to make the driver feel as if he has some kind of control over the vehicle.

It is an illusion.

The first car I ever owned had a speedometer, an oil gauge, an amp meter and a thermometer on the radiator. This equipment was a great convenience and indispensable since the ability to monitor every important part of the car whilst moving was of great importance. One always had to be prepared to top up with water or even carry out running repairs. I once repaired the magneto on the Alvis with a safety pin. I knew what had happened when the engine cut out. I did not need a light to tell me. Now 21st century man needs a warning light to inform him that he's left the handbrake on, as if he could move without noticing it.

It makes me wonder whether the lights came before the idiot or the idiot before the lights.

Every conceivable operation in this Subaru is monitored with a warning or location light. Everything's got a light, handbrake, door handle, seat belt, 12 preset buttons on the radio, the CD player, oil warning light, brake pad light, seat belt warning light, electric window button light, central locking light, all are illuminated giving me instant information and thus making me feel in control of the machine! But – and herein lieth the rub – if any one of the lights were to go out there is nothing I can do about it except take the beast to the nearest dealer. Who will plug it into a computer and find out what is wrong and since modern cars never go wrong the whole array of lights is pointless and for idiots. In fact the manufacturer could get away with making a car with less instrumentation and lights than Mr Alvis did when he made my first car in 1927. A nice round speedometer and a fuel gauge is all that's needed. Not only that but a GPS device tells me that six satellites are tracking me. The mobile phone sends out a blue light. I have only to shout at the dashboard for the phone to operate.

It is voice-activated.

The machine understands what I say.

It will repeat what I ask it to do.

It will talk back at me.

My father would never have believed it.

Mr Alvis would never have believed it.

Mr Rolls and Mr Royce would never have believed it.

Not only that but none of the above, who were by the

way very intelligent men, would ever believe that within the lifetime of their children a Mr Google would invent a car that would move along the Queen's highway without a driver!

The building I am looking at is an example of pure vernacular architecture. No plans were made on paper for it. The plans were in the craftsman's head. He could see the building before it was built.

Today plans have to be submitted to planning departments and then passed by planning committees comprised of people who have no idea what they are looking at, but providing that the proposed new building is like an old building which never had planning permission in the first place, then the new building will get a green light.

The building I am looking at has a corrugated sheet iron roof. It is painted tar black. It was once straw thatch. Before it was thatch it could have been turf.

The building I am looking at in the fading evening light is probably sitting on the foundations of a building that was standing when King Offa built his dyke.

The doctor comes out. His name is Gutsell, David Gutsell.

Gutsell means good soul in auld Saxon.

I lower the window.

My doctor leans over.

"Mr Corbet has had a stroke and one of the side effects of the stroke is that he cannot swallow, or move his left arm. He's going in."

The doctor pauses.

He takes a deep breath and tells me, "There is no phone, there is no phone in that house."

"It's a Saxon long house."

The doctor shakes his head. He is wearing an open-necked shirt. He scratches his neck.

"There's a phone box a mile back down the road," I said.

"The mobile, we'll use the mobile."

I shook my head. "No signal."

41

"Use the other mobile we have two, don't we?"

"No signal on either."

"Ninety five per cent of the country is covered."

"We are in the 5% part."

The doctor sneezes. He wipes his nose squeezing it between his thumb and finger. I hand him a Kleenex.

"Are you good with dogs?" he asks.

"All right," I reply.

"The dog keeps looking at me."

"He's going to, a dog's only got one master."

"That's what I'm worried about."

"What sort of dog is it?"

"A collie."

"They got more intelligence than the average human," I said.

I follow the doctor.

"We have two problems," the doctor says. "If he does not go in, Mr Corbet needs a home help to ease his life a little. Second problem is that his house is not fit for human habitation. He defecates in the barn with the animals."

I walk with the doctor into the house and into a time warp.

Into a hypothetical dimension of quantum physics called a parallel universe from a thousand years ago.

All I have to do is to imagine that the roof of the long house is made of turf and not corrugated sheet iron.

This is practically the only difference.

In other respects the place is exactly the same as a Saxon long house was one thousand years ago.

A three-point border collie smells us.

Mr Corbet lifts his right arm with his left hand.

It is a gesture.

He is sitting at the kitchen table. The table stands on a flagstone floor. There is an open range with an oven each side. The embers still glow. There is a clockwork trivet, to cook meat or game. There is a pump, a real hand-operated pump with a spout over a stone sink.

"Mind your head," and the doctor points out a pair of plain wires hung on insulated hooks once used for suspending the wires on an electric fence. A pair of crocodile clips connect wires to a lamp socket. A Honda generator hums away in the distance. As the freezer kicks in the light goes dim and the generator changes its drone. A ledged braced and battened door leads to a room on the right. An identical door leads to that part of the house where the cows lived. The door is open. There are no animals. The aroma of hay hangs in the background.

Forty years ago I stopped in a house right in the middle of France; that part of France called the Massif Central. The house was almost the same. There were 20 cows in the milking manger. It was the middle of winter 20 below outside, 20 inside. The house had mains electricity. They made 28 Saint Nectaire cheeses every month. They were sold six months in advance to five-star restaurants. I looked into the barn. I saw the toilet roll hanging on a nail, just like it had been in France.

But, the home help will not be able to crap in the barn. The home help will not be able to use the water from the pump, which comes up from a well. If she drinks a drop of the said water she will vomit and have diarrhoea for a week. There are hardly any modern working surfaces except the table. There are a million refuges for insects and bacteria in the walls of the house.

It is primitive beyond belief but Mr Corbet has never been ill before in his life and he is 87. Mr Corbet goes out to the pub every evening at ten to nine. He sits in the same chair; his chair in the corner and the dog curls up in front of the fire. The reason we are here is because Mr Corbet did not go out to the pub last night. He was missed. Word got out.

"Jim Corbet never called in for a pint."

The gamekeeper was told.

He told Nobby Clark who then told Joe Price. Jack Adams was told and started to worry about the dominoes.

The situation was grave.

Jack Adams sent his son out on his trial bike.

He had a mobile phone but had to go back home to make the call to the doctor.

About two miles away is a Norman chapel. It is in the middle of a field. It was dedicated to the lady who became a saint, St Milborough. On the walls of this chapel are the stools and crutches of cripples who had once been healed there. They had faith. The man in the long house has the same kind of faith. The man in the long house does not trust modern medicine. Every illness he caught during his long life he cured by a positive state of mind.

I look at Mr Corbet. He does not want to go to hospital. He tries to stand. The chair is pushed back. The dog moves towards his master. The doctor moves towards Mr Corbet. The dog growls. Mr Corbet looks at his dog.

The dog knows.

Mr Corbet and the doctor move towards the other door. When the doctor opens the door, I see that it is a bedroom and a storeroom.

The dog growls.

My doctor wants to examine or talk to Mr Corbet in private.

The dog knows.

I sit on a chair. The dog places its head on my knee.

I scratch behind the animal's ears, remembering all the time that my old dog enjoyed the same kind of caressing.

There is a Welsh dresser in the room. It is covered in brasses from Shire horse harnesses. Mr Corbet must sit for hours polishing them. Hanging from a nail is some kind of calendar with the sign of the Zodiac in the top right hand corner. Its purpose is to list the holy days, the saints' days. Like the room the calendar belongs to a world that is long vanished, but is has not vanished, I am here in it.

There is an *Old Moore's Almanac* on the middle shelf. My father used to have it. He swore by it. He planted his crops by it. It was used in his daily routine, it gave the schedule of the earth and it prophesied the end of the world.

I scratch the dog. The dog looks up at me. The dog knows. Eventually my doctor comes out of the room.

"Let's make Mr Corbet a cup of tea," he said.

I look at the doctor. I stand up. I move away from the dog. The dog looks at me. I see the white enamel side of a propane gas cooker. It is inside an alcove. There is a great burnt black kettle sitting on a gas ring. I have never used a hand-operated water pump before. It works. The water looks clean. To make sure I cup it in my hand. It is cold. It is clean. I fill the kettle. I look for matches. There are none that I could find. I pull a lighter out of my pocket and light the stove.

The doctor finds the tea caddy. It is full. There is a pantry. It has a slate shelf. The pantry is cool. There is a pint of milk. A loaf of bread. Home cured ham. Home made pickled onions. Jam with pips. Shelves of tinned food. It smells good, like an old fashioned pantry should.

"We have lift off," I said.

"It is remarkable."

"It's not that dirty."

"He's not going in."

"It's just rough."

"He thinks he can swallow."

The doctor smiles. "He's got a sister."

"Where?"

"Knighton."

"She on the phone?"

"I have the number," the doctor nods.

The kettle boils. The brown teapot still has leaves in it. I fill it from the pump, swilling the pot. The leaves become trapped in the sink. I warm the pot. I make the tea. We cannot find the sugar. The doctor goes to ask Mr Corbet where the sugar is. I find three mugs. They are stained.

"I don't believe it, he can talk," the doctor said shaking his head from side to side.

"He's decided that he ain't goin' in," I said.

The doctor shakes his head.

The tea is ready.

Mr Corbet shuffles back into the room. His arm swings. We all sit around the table. The dog puts his head on Mr Corbet's knee. We all sip tea.

I break the silence.

"Corbet means Corbo which means Crow in old French," I say.

The doctor and I watch Mr Corbet swallow.

"Cross breeds is stronger, boyo," Mr Corbet says, and he opens his mouth and there is only a very slight lisp.

"You're going to have to see a physiotherapist about that arm," the doctor says.

I get up, I'm going to get the drug box from the car.

Whilst the doctor is dispensing the drugs I ask Mr Corbet whether or not he would like a fire.

"There's some cock wood around the corner," he says pointing towards that part of the house that was also a stable.

The cock wood has been chopped from unwanted pallets. The logs are well seasoned. In a few minutes the fire is spitting sparks. Every time I go out for logs the dog follows and every time I reach for a log the dog licks my hand. I build Mr Corbet a fire that will last him all night because I sense that he might sit up with his dog digesting what had happened to his body.

By the time the doctor and I had finished our work dusk had melted into a blue-tinted night. Only the brightest stars are in the sky. It is a strange light. As I lift the rear door of the car to replace the drug bag I see the silhouette of the Brown Clee. There is a glowing pulsing brightness above the mountain. The doctor and I look at the sky. It is as if we were in a saucer, as if we were in the centre of a great round valley and that something was about to materialise over in the west.

"It's the Northern Lights," I said.

"The *aurora borealis.*"

"The Eskimos think that it's the place where the souls of the dead go, a parallel universe."

"Mr Corbet's not going there yet."

"What about the home help?" I asked.

"No home help, but I know a district nurse who is married to a farmer, she will keep an eye on him."

"Outside the system."

"No tick boxes."

"You have the correct surname."

"Oh."

"Good soul, Gutsell means good soul in old Saxon."

"I'll betch'a he goes to the pub," I said as I started the car.

"And leave that spitting fire."

"He'll put that big fire guard in front of it."

"Dangerous."

"Domino night, he'll go to the pub."

As I drive down the valley towards my town, the aurora borealis disappears.

I look at the illuminated dashboard.

I am in a space ship.

Moving out of one dimension and into another.

Back to base.

And everything is fine.

Just fine.

5   Intelligent Mynah Bird

WE HAD A WEEK AND THREE DAYS of hot sunshine. The combines were out all night in the fields reaping the harvest.

During Wednesday afternoon the sky had been swept by gusts of warm wind. Vast long silvery white clouds were cut lengthways like awesome furrows. The diagram of the thunderstorm to come was being etched into the blue sky. The heavens were being charged full of concealed electricity like a giant battery. One could not see the loaded magnetic fields but you could feel the trembling of discharged energy.

Wednesday evening and I looked through the window towards the Welsh hills and imagined lost stratospheric galleries along which claps of thunder would eventually roll.

I imagined that Google was hidden inside a distant maze of artificial vaults.

I was looking up plastics and polyethylene, which is used instead of olive oil for lubricating skin creams and other cleaning solutions.

It was half past six and I was waiting for Dr Pyke who would not arrive until a quarter to seven. He had lent me a book called *The World Without Us*.

It is a vision of the future without humans.

There was already a call on the screen. I looked up at the electric quartz clock. The hands said 6:40. I decided to print the call sheet. As the printer finished pushing out the sheet of paper Dr Pyke walked in.

"If this man is right," I said to Dr Pyke after he had logged in on his computer in the doctor's consulting room, "it is not only used for lubricating skin cream but they also use them to clean paint which means that not only do they go down the drain but they also get carried all over the place in the wind."

I was holding the book open at Chapter Nine, 'Polymers are forever'.

"Just like pollen," Dr Pyke said, "but and unlike pollen which will disappear because it is natural, polyethylene beads in paint remover will remain for ever and a day."

"So what you have is something in the atmosphere far worse than fumes from a car," I said.

"We have been burning petrol since Roman times," Dr Pyke said, "it's a Roman name, *Petra Oleum*, the substance that seeped from the earth in Modena, Italy. The fuel that fired the flames of the ancient Gods, we have been burning it for probably thousands of years. But micro fine polyethylene beads have been released into the atmosphere only very recently, like five years ago and they do not disappear, they are here for ever and ever until time ends."

"So not only do they bung up the little arseholes of lug worms at the bottom of the ocean they could also be bunging up the bum holes of bees," I said.

"We do not know, but what is sure is that the polyethylene beads that land on flowers like pollen do not do bumble bees or any other insects any good." Dr Pyke said.

"And when the insects go ..." I said.

"We are the master race and it's almost run."

"I'll make coffee," I said, "before we run up the A49 because there is a patient who has run out of drugs and does not have a car and lives in the middle of a housing estate without knowing anyone who can collect his drugs for him."

"You mean to tell me that we are a delivery service for patients who forget to collect prescriptions?" Dr Pyke said.

"Is what I am reading from this call sheet," I said waving it in the air.

Dr Pyke took the call sheet from me and read it.

"You're right, make the coffee first," he said.

"And all you have to do is to hand it to him," I said.

"Or put it through the letterbox," Dr Pyke said.

"No, what you have to do is to draw some water from the tap in a glass, push a pill from out of the foil packaging and then place it next to him and then tell him how to drink it."

"Wipe his arse," Dr Pyke said.

"Ask him if he wants a crap first, then wait. Get it in the right order, you're a doctor," I said.

It was 7.30 when we hit the road and the evening was warm and swollen with the breath of an expected storm. It was also a darker dusk than it should have been until a flash of lightning lit the sky.

We both looked and saw that the electric pylon on the side of the road had become for a few seconds a silver silhouette.

"Did you see that?" we both said in unison.

And the ear holes on the sides of our heads waited for the thunder.

When the explosion came it was like an aural snapshot followed by physical vibrations inside the car.

We looked at each other and the looking was asking the question, if the whole thing really did start with a big bang then how much bigger was it than this one?

Was there something else?

Would there be an encore?

We were moving up a gradient.

The concrete gutter next to the Armco barrier overflowed. The car moved into a mist. We smelt the rain. We could see the very edge of the ozone. I looked at it. I could taste it. It was that part of the atmosphere where ether congregates, where faxes get lost, where emails disappear, where lightning is made.

We were moving along at 60.

We were moving along 50.

We were doing 45 when we hit surface water.

We went into a cloudburst and the Subaru did not flinch, it did not move an inch.

I took a fast look in the rear view mirror.

The Subaru was leaving a cloud of spray like an F1 car and she felt as solid as a rock. Not only that but her tyres were making a sound like an illegitimate musical instrument. It was an environmental noise expanding towards a totality close to the infinite.

"The window must be open just a crack, I'll close it," Dr Pyke said.

But nothing happened.

"If we were not delivering a drug to someone who forgot to collect his drugs then we would not experience this," I said.

"We could leave the road and enter into eternity in a bubble of spray before we get there," Dr Pyke said.

"There would then be an inquiry," I said.

"You would certainly have a lot of forms to fill in," Dr Pyke said.

"No," I said, "we both would because the inquiry would be into why 28 tablets of Furosemide had to be delivered by a doctor and a driver at a cost of 400 pounds."

"Why?" Dr Pyke asked.

"Because that is how much each visit costs," I said.

There are occasions when the phenomenon known as a 'white-out' arrives. It is usually caused by snow or fog. It is when everything becomes white. When there is nothing, no features, nothing to relate to, neither up nor down, no right or left and nothing ahead. It is like driving into a screen. It is very scary. As I moved in a northerly direction a 30-ton truck came out of a wall of water. It was a liquid white-out. All the truck's lights were illuminated, they were all on full beam and what was more the thing was displacing more water with its 18 wheels than goes over Dinham weir in a week.

The water knocked the car sideways, which was fortunate because the end of the unit was on the wrong side of the road. At the very same time as the car instinctively moved into the gutter the God Thor threw another thunderbolt at the surface of the road. When the bolt exploded Dr Pyke gripped the handle over the door so tightly that he inadvertently lifted himself off his seat.

"Shit," he said.

"When did you last light a candle in a church?" I shouted.

"I can't remember," Dr Pyke shouted back.

"It pays to ask for divine protection now and again," I said.

I had to slow down to less than 20 miles an hour because there was a brown river running down the embankment like a waterfall. The cloudburst was washing a layer of topsoil right through the bottom of a hawthorn hedge and over the road. The potatoes had been machine picked. The soil was loose. It was coming through the hedge like a weir. I stopped. I selected low ratio. The Subaru ploughed into the layer of topsoil. The wheels spun before they gripped the tarmac.

"All we need is another truck coming at us and we will go into eternity all for the sake of a box of pills," I said trying to steer the car out of a sideways slide.

And the strange thing was that it was a very localised storm because as the car came out of the mire on the wrong side of the road there was no rain, just drizzle and what was more the vehicles coming at us had their wipers on intermittent, which told another story.

"They'll all be waltzing to the tune of Strauss when they hit the mud," I said.

Ten minutes later Tom-Tom took us right outside the required door.

Whilst I waited for Dr Pyke to deliver the 28 Furosemide tablets I entered a London address into Tom-Tom. I then asked the thing to do a dry run. I watched the screen moving at the speed of light as it worked out all the roads and motorways.

It told me that it was 175 miles from where I was to Number 10 Downing Street, and that it would take me four hours to get there.

I can never get my head around how Tom-Tom does it but it is a frightful nightmare. I mean you could without doubt nail one right onto the end of a missile and it would take 1000 tons of TNT right though the Prime Minister's letterbox!

What's more a missile would travel as the crow flies and would not take four hours to get there.

It is more than a wonder that the powers that be allow such a thing to be sold over the counter not only that but you can even buy the things from Amazon!

As Dr Pyke buckled himself into his seat the phone rang and told us that we had a call in Diddlebury.

Dr Pyke reached for the laptop. Dr Pyke studied the call.

"Back in the eighteen hundreds I had a great great grandfather who lived in Diddlebury. He was an Inoculator," Dr Pyke said.

"What's an Inoculator?" I asked as I negotiated a mini roundabout, which would be lethal to anyone on two wheels.

"Jenner invented a vaccine which prevented smallpox," Dr Pyke said.

"The Pox," I said, "Shakespeare uses the expression; 'Pox on it I'll not meddle with it'."

"Jenner eradicated it," Dr Pyke said, "He noticed that milkmaids very rarely suffered from smallpox. That they always had a very good complexion, whereas others who had had the pox and survived had pock marks all over their face."

"They had cream on their face," I said.

"No," Dr Pyke said," boils, as and when the boils on the cow disgorged pus, the milkmaid, who would inadvertently touch the eruption became immunised against the disease."

"So why inject it into the bloodstream, why not just rub it on the skin?" I asked.

"In fact what Jenner did was to make two small cuts on a boy's arm and then pour liquid from cow pox into the wound," Dr Pyke said.

"The milkmaids must have ingested it through wounds, or splits on their fingers, chaps or cold sores," I said.

"It was the first form of vaccination and it comes from the Latin word *Vacca* which means cow," Dr Pyke said.

"Which sounds better than a Cowination," I said.

It started to rain big spots. I turned the wipers to double time. I switched the lights on. The ditches were overflowing. The water was becoming browner, meaning that we were moving into that part where the great cloud had burst. And I thought about it. How on earth does so much water hang up in the air? I mean, it is not held up there in a container it just sort of floats about in a cloud until it's ready to fall. But what makes it burst all at once all over the place? Like a balloon full of water bursting. Bang. As if the Gods were throwing water bombs at each other.

"So what did Jenner have to do with great granddad Pyke?" I asked. After replacing cloudburst thoughts back into the limbic part of my brain.

"Nothing, it all came later," Dr Pyke said." At first nobody wanted to have anything to do with Jenner and the pox doctor. It was Napoleon. He was worried about the health of his army since more men were dying of the pox than anything else including fighting. So the Emperor contacted Jenner and had all his army inoculated and none of then caught the pox! And after the Napoleonic wars the English medical profession realised how effective inoculation was and so surgeons became inoculators and created their own vaccines from cow pox and injected it using syringes."

"No disposables," I said.

"No Aids,"

"No litigation."

"No insurance."

"No NHS."

"The elimination of disease."

"The medicalization of life."

"My great great granddad, the inoculator, made his own vaccine," Dr Pyke said proudly.

"The one who used to chase patients up the Corve Dale

with their trousers around their ankles before shoving a great syringe into one of their bum cheeks right up to where it says 'Sheffield' on the handle," I said.

Laughter.

I looked at Tom-Tom. The wipers were doing double time. I saw water running off fields. It was brown. I slowed. I hit another mud monsoon without using low gear.

The car held.

"Only two miles to our destination," I said.

It was up a drive. A 45-degree rutted drive with twin streams running on each rut like rivers. And the strange thing is that when you drive up a drive at such an angle you cannot see anything because you are leaning back and you have to pull yourself forward in order to see where you are going, which did not matter that much because the ruts held the wheels like railway lines.

When we had climbed for about 440 yards we came to a yard with a large black corrugated sheet iron barn facing a white bungalow. The road in the drive became level and I was able to turn left and cross the yard. As the car approached the building an automatic halogen floodlight illuminated. I could see that the yard was well drained and showed only surface water.

Dr Pyke opened the door and got out.

Dr Pyke opened the rear door and lifted out his bag. He walked towards the front door.

Only what I assumed to be the living room had any lights on. Dr Pyke waited. Nobody came to the door. I got out of the car and walked towards the window off the room that had the lights on. Through a crack in the curtains I saw a woman sitting in a chair. She wanted to move. There was a Collie dog looking at her. The dog also turned towards the door.

"Try the door, she's in the chair, there is a dog but it's a Collie," I said.

Dr Pyke opened the door. The dog came to the door. The

dog was wagging its tail. Dr Pyke went in. I went back to the car.

I hit the button that activates the phone. The device told me that I had dialled Dispatch. I wondered if the voice had started out as a human voice or if it was a wholly electronic voice. Dispatch answered, it was a human. I gave the time of arrival.

I hit the radio.

Pictures at an Exhibition.

Mussorgsky.

Night on a Bare Mountain.

I listened to both pieces.

Dr Pyke came out of the house.

"Our task is not yet done, is the printer charged?" he asked.

"Fully," I replied.

"Have we got paper for it?"

I nodded.

"I am going to type an admission letter."

Dr Pyke started typing on the Rugged laptop. I switched the printer on. The blue light flickered. I set up the printer and loaded it with a few sheets of paper. The whole caboodle is wireless, which means that I have no idea how it works. When a system is wired together I can understand that the electrical impulses running through wires carry information, which is decoded by the receiving device rather like the electrical intranet, which is the nervous system in the human body. Break the nerve and nothing happens. Break the spinal cord and the human is knackered, dead from the waist down!

Methinks that it will not be long before a blue tooth neurotransmitter is invented that will fire information from the brain across the gap in a broken spine. Of course there might be a problem if the human fitted with such a device was in the same room as a blue tooth DVD player sending out signals into a plasma screen. It could be that his brain would pick up unwanted signals. It could be that eventually the human brain will be able to watch a film directly inside its cerebral cortex if the right decoder is fitted.

Pyke finished typing.

The printer came to life.

It swallowed the paper.

It spat it out.

"Pity there is no way to print the envelope," Dr Pyke said as he opened the door.

"You could email," I said.

"Get lost, better and safer to give it to the ambulance driver," Dr Pyke said.

As Dr Pyke walked across the yard the halogen light came on. It was windy. The light picked up the waves in the puddles of water.

Five minutes later Dr Pyke came out of the house.

When he got into the car he said, "She won't go in because of Joe."

"Joe? that the dog's name?" I asked.

"The dog is called Sam and is not the problem, the problem is the Mynah bird," Dr Pyke said.

"They can talk, some can talk so well that they can make complete sentences," I said.

"Not only does Joe talk but he also mimics the ring sound of a telephone, I lifted the receiver twice on account of the flaming bird," Dr Pyke said.

"So what happens next?" I asked.

"She won't leave the bird and the bird goes with the dog," Dr Pyke said.

"They got a budgerigar in the hospital," I said, "ambulance men brought it in with a patient. Nurses cover it at night with a cloth over the cage."

"Joe has to go to her daughter in Bridgnorth," Dr Pyke said.

"Daughter fetches the dog and bird then," I said.

"Daughter can't fetch the dog or bird because her husband erects mobile phone towers and is away from home except weekends." Dr Pyke said.

"So what happens next?"

"We take the dog and the bird to the daughter."

"What if we get a call and we are in the middle of Bridgnorth where we should not be and the call is right out the other side of New Radnor or somewhere else more than a three days' camel ride away? I mean like old Stan Jones is about due to pull out his catheter, which he does every other day and that's Hereford Road, Presteigne, we get a call out there and we are right up a flaming gum tree. We can drop ourselves right in the shit if we start moving animals about like the RSPCA," I said.

"This woman has had a heart op. I think the valve's bleeding, she's got to go in without worrying about her animals, make her feel better," Dr Pyke said.

"You asked for a blue light then?" I said.

Dr Pyke nodded.

"They'll come from the Arms, they're gonna be here in 10 minutes. Let's go have a look at the situation," I said.

As we both walked across the yard I saw the dog waiting for us in the doorway.

"You'll get me locked up, Pyke," I said.

As we walked over the threshold the dog barked.

"Shut up Sam," and you could tell that it was the voice of a talking bird.

The patient was sitting on a brown leather sofa. Her three-point border collie was licking her hand. He wagged his tail. He inspected us moving in a sort of circular motion watching us all the time as if we were sheep.

The black Mynah bird was in a cage. The creature looked at me with its head on one side using its right eye.

A phone rang.

"It's the bird," Dr Pyke said.

It was the bird but you couldn't tell that the sound was not that of a real telephone. I looked at the patient. She was almost white. Anaemic. She raised her hand. She pointed towards the kitchen. Dr Pyke lowered his ear towards her.

"It's all in a cupboard, in the kitchen," she whispered.

"It's in the cupboard in the kitchen," Dr Pyke said.

It was where the bird and dog food was stored.

I found special Mynah bird pellets together with soft food like plums and prunes. It was all in a plastic tray. The dog food was on the floor. I placed four tins in another plastic tray. I made two journeys to the car. I placed both trays on top of the drug boxes.

The Mynah bird had dropped about five stools.

The cage stank.

I opened the door of the bird's cage.

"Go away," the bird shouted.

I looked at the bird's beak. I did not want the smell of Mynah bird shit in the car. I gathered together the newspaper on the bottom of the cage folding it over so that the bird's stools were wrapped. I walked into the yard followed by the dog and dumped the parcel into a green bin.

"He's here again," the bird shouted as I entered the room.

I found a copy of *The Times*.

I opened the bird's cage all the time watching the black creature. I folded the ends the newspaper so that they fitted correctly in the bottom of the cage.

A blue light strobed up the drive.

A blue light strobed in the yard.

The dog started to whine.

"More boys, more boys," the bird shouted.

The paramedics came into the room.

Dr Pyke talked to them.

The patient started to tremble. She made scared sounds.

The biggest of the paramedics sat next to her.

I took the dog out of the room holding it by its collar.

As I closed the door the bird shouted the dog's name.

"Sam, Sam, come back Sam," the bird called.

I waited in the kitchen scratching behind the dog's ears. It looked at me. The dog understood. I thanked God that it was a collie. Had it been a German Shepherd or any other less intelligent beast then there could have been an abundance of problems.

When the paramedics took the patient out the dog pulled towards the stretcher and raised its head. The woman dropped her hand. The dog licked it.

"Gone, gone, all gone," the bird shouted and then it went ballistic, jumping up and down in its cage all the time calling out for the dog. "Sam, Sam," it called and it sounded human.

The dog and I watched the ambulance slide into the ruts.

I spotted a pile of hessian sacks in the barn. They were dry. I took two of them. I placed them on the back seat of the car.

"Come on," I said to the dog.

The dog followed me to the car. He jumped onto the back seat.

I went inside to collect the bird.

It looked at me. I lifted the cage holding it by its handle.

"Holidays," the bird said.

When I placed it on the back seat next to the dog it said "Hello Sam."

The dog wagged its tail, thumping the seat.

Dr Pyke locked the door to the house placing the key on a hook underneath the eaves.

"Holidays," the bird said as the car door shut.

Just before we arrived at Morville, where the road dips we saw mud. There had been a massive mudslide.

"In fact you can trace the storm right across the county, it moved in an arc as if it scribed a kind of circular motion," I said.

"We'll be in a circular motion if we get stuck in that lot," Dr Pyke said.

"What do we do?" I asked, "we ain't even supposed to be here and we're lumbered with two animals. I'm going right through that mud," I said.

I looked at it and judged that all that would happen would be that the wheels would spin until they found the hard road surface, anyway the slide was only about twenty feet across.

As the car moved into the mud a telephone started to ring. I looked at Dr Pyke and he looked at me. It was the sound of a telephone inside a house, an old fashioned telephone. The bird was good. The mud scraped the underside of the car. The wheels spun. It was the sort of thing you wanted to do to a car but never have the chance.

The wheels spun spreading mud as we moved past the old church.

"When we get to the daughter's, I'll phone Dispatch and tell them that we have finished the call. It will give us half an hour's grace," I said.

"They'll never be any the wiser, no one will ever know about this," Dr Pyke said.

"Looks like we cracked it," I said.

As I drove towards Bridgnorth the bird started to ring like a telephone and the dog wagged its tail.

"I wonder if that bird can swear," I said.

"No, it just makes ring tones," Dr Pyke said.

"A bird like that should have a few bad swear words in its vocabulary, shouldn't you?" I said turning to look at the thing sitting behind its bars.

"Fucking holidays," the bird replied.

The light was on. The rendezvous was made. The bird and the dog were on holiday.

I was happy. Dr Pyke was happy. The road had dried out. I hit 85 on the straight.

We were listening to Classic FM.

As we went up the road out of Aston Munslow doing 75 the *1812 Overture* started.

I turned the volume right up.

A pair of six-pound smoothbore bronze cannons and a twelve-pound Howitzer went off as we entered the hospital car park.

Coffee.

6   *The Last Debutante*

2:30 ON THE AM.

Gusts of wind sweeping the earth.

Whirlwinds.

Leaves together with discarded fast food styrofoam containers turning into spiral staircases.

A bicycle tyre hanging on a streetlight swinging like a hangman's noose.

Plastic bags and leaves caught in a chicken wire fence sending out vibrations like Buddhist prayer flags.

In the far corner of the supermarket car park a fox foraging for food.

I touched the window button on the door. As it cracked open the sound of the fox's shrill bark bounced across the empty car park. Beyond at the edge of the peripheral I heard the sound of a goods train turn into a trapped drone as it moved through the station.

The phone in the car rang.

The fox looked up.

I reached out to touch the phone.

I looked for the fox.

Gone.

Sucked into the crevices of the night.

It started to rain. Big spots. They bounced off the bonnet. I reached out for my folder. The dispatcher wanted us to go to the other end of the zone.

"Had I got 'The Rugged' switched on?"

"Affirmative," I replied.

'The Rugged' is a laptop, which is supposed to be indestructible. It operates via half a dozen satellites. Supposedly it will stand being run over or even dropped from a great height. It is a strange instrument with a mind of its own, meaning that it will cease to work, shut down or just freeze without reason. It is such an unreliable device that on occasion the urge to throw it right out of the window overcomes all reasonable thought. If anyone had the balls to do it there would be is a cheer from both doctor and driver as the thing bounced on the tarmac. The trouble is that since the thing costs at least two and a half grand the driver would eventually turn round and retrieve it, which is the reason it is indestructible.

However, when it does work it's a brilliant device, enabling the doctor to look at all the medical notes of the patient, and the driver the address, complete with post code which he will feed into Tom-Tom and then be guided by another set of satellites orbiting our planet a couple of hundred miles above our heads.

Wise and wonderful are the works of a wheelbarrow.

I read the address on 'The Rugged'.

Brampton Castle, better known as the 'Black Keep', so called by the Welsh who called the Normans 'The Black Gentiles' on account of the fact that the Normans stole all their land and then raped and murdered their way along that part of the land they called Marches, all the time calling 'Taffy' a thief.

The dreaded Marcher Lords or the Black Gentiles, cruel bastards who ruled with a rod of iron.

What I had on the call sheet was the notes concerning an aristocratic female living in a castle situated on the Marches who was suffering from manic depression. She had been drinking vodka but not doubles and had projectile vomited up a double decaf latte together with an almond croissant.

I could not figure out whether or not she was actually in the Castle or the lodge.

I have a system. Never start out on a call until you know exactly where the person is. It could be that there is no mobile reception or that Tom-Tom does not have the knowledge. The golden rule is never trust technology in the Marches because once you arrive at where you think you should be there will be nothing there. Not only that but even signposts in the Marches are masterpieces of disinformation. A sign will lure you towards a place, you will go right past and then you will find another sign pointing you in the direction you have just come from.

Always phone ahead.

I reached out towards the phone. I hit the buttons and listened to the dial tone. I imagined that the phone I had caused to ring was a wall-mounted device made by Charles Williams jnr in 1882. The one with a hand-cranked magneto for generating the ringing tone in a distant number. No other device would be suitable for a stately home run by the National Trust and what's more there would be a preservation order on it.

I was aware of the rain drumming on the roof of the car.

It was ringing. I waited.

"Hello,"

"This is the doctor's driver, where are you?"

A voice took a deep breath before it let out the words into the mouthpiece.

An aristocratic voice, "Do you know the Bog on the Moor where the great forest of Aston Moor is?"

"Where the Templar church is?"

"Yes, now if you drive through the main gate you will see another gate. It is where the lodge is. Go through that gate and follow the track. After a quarter of a mile you will see the hunting lodge. It is where we are residing at the moment. Mobile telephones do not work on the left side of the common, GPS devices do not work either, there is something in the rocks."

"The rocks."

"The geographical location is not suitable for any kind of wireless device."

"Is the lodge on the left side?"

"Yes."

"It is a good job I phoned you."

"Yes."

"Which gate is it?"

"Where are you coming from?"

"East."

"The main gate, hurry she is ill."

And then I heard a bakelite sound. The aristocrat had hung the earpiece onto his wall-mounted hand cranked phone.

It was raining.

Big spots.

There were many of them all close together. It was like being under a waterfall. And rain is that most magical of things because you cannot understand how it remains up there in such abundant quantities until just the right time.

Who pulls the plug?

God?

I sat in the car. Ronald Smith played Scriabin.

Sonata No. 9. The Black Mass.

I waited.

Dr Dorothy James opened the rear door. She threw her Gladstone bag onto the rear seat. She opened the front door. She lifted her skirt with her right hand. She sat in the seat. She looked at me. Her hair was wet. She reached into the glove compartment. She removed a white tissue. She removed her glasses. She wiped her face. She sneezed. Whilst she removed rain from her spectacles she looked at me holding the call sheet.

"Where are we going?"

"To the other side of the zone."

"Who?"

"An aristocrat in a castle."

"At half past two in the morning?"

"Because her private doctor does not work out of hours."

"Brampton Castle."

"Where's that?"

"The Black Keep, near the Golden Valley, the Templar Knights built the church."

"In the castle?"

"Next to it."

"How far?"

"One hour, 30 miles."

My doctor sighed.

The car moved and the rain bounced off the bonnet. It bounced so high that it came back down and bounced again.

It rained. Big Spots.

The water was kerb high.

Out on the main road where there were no kerbs the water on the road was level with the grass verge.

Because the hedges had been cut with a mechanical device the remains of the butchered vegetation had blocked the drains. The ditches were full. Water was running from the surface of ploughed fields. The brown water ran onto the road. I was driving on mud. It was exciting. Dr James hung onto the handle above the door.

Going around the Serpent the Subaru moved like a giant crab. It was a sideways motion and a miracle that the car stopped before hitting the crash barrier.

The Subaru struggled. All the wheels spun. And the car moved away back into the middle of the road and in the correct direction.

It was that time of year when it gets dark at seven and light at seven. The equinox.

Equal day and equal night.

The rain had stopped but the wind roared across the racecourse and the clouds passed across the profile of the moon like woolly sheep. And the moon grew continually brighter and brighter and all of a sudden the wind blew itself out and we were driving down the main road where the railway goes over the road and I saw that there were no cats eyes.

Instead there was a great duck pond right under the bridge. I almost continued right into the centre of it.

My doctor and I leaned forward the better to see it.

"How deep is it?" my doctor asked.

"We'll get a pretty good idea when that truck goes through it," I said.

I reversed. I moved back. And we waited.

The truck had enough lights attached to it to melt black ice. I flashed my lights at the driver encouraging him to proceed. The truck pushed a bow wave of water like the *Queen Mary*. It appeared to be as deep as the vehicle's front bumper which was of the stainless steel variety and immense.

"I am not going through that," I said, looking up at the rear view mirror because a car was coming behind me at a considerable rate of knots.

The car was a red Ford Escort. It pulled up behind me. The driver was young. He had a female with him.

When the truck had passed the driver behind flashed his lights. I did not move. The driver of the car behind pulled out and around me and then stopped beside me. He made the sign that told me I was a wanker. I took no notice but instead looked down at his passenger a female, about 18 with a full balcony.

"No," I said.

But he drove right into the water and what was more he even changed up a gear and he made a wave almost as big as the truck until he was right under the railway bridge where he stopped dead.

"The water has moved into his engine through the air filter," I said.

"Which means that the electrics have all gone funny," my doctor said.

"Worse, it was a diesel, he's cracked the head, the car is completely knackered," I said.

"How can we help?" my doctor said.

"Can't," I said, "wet feet, they are going to get wet feet and we do not want wet feet because we have to go on a visit to an aristocrat who has been drinking vodka but not doubles and has projectile vomited up a double decaf latte together with an almond croissant."

"Can't we do something?" my doctor said.

"No," I said, "what can we do? We can't help an idiot. It is a small part of his learning curve. He will never do that again."

We waited for them to get out of the car.

Nothing happened.

I did a three-point turn.

I would go a different way.

Tom-Tom kept telling me to turn round when possible.

It took another three-quarters of an hour to reach our destination. The car never once exceeded 30 mph. My doctor never spoke a word. She just hung onto the handle above her head. She was looking for more duck ponds. We never found one. In spite of an abundance of water on the sides of the road, it never met in the middle.

I stopped the Subaru when I saw the gate. It was a large wrought iron gate hanging on stone pillars. The gate was open. Each side of the drive there was an avenue of trees. The leaves were falling. The wind was blowing and it was raining. Real rain. There were branches lying on the road. We were miles from anywhere. The Marches. The old Normans built hundreds of castles along the border. There are more castles per square mile in our zone than anywhere else in the world. The Bastard King gave each Norman knight thousands of acres of land. The Knights built their castles on the land. The Marcher lords still live in them.

I saw a National Trust sign. It was green.

The gold letters said:

Brampton Castle
East Gate
Visitors

I visualised gates on the tips of each compass point. We both looked for the other gate. The one the Earl had told us to look for. The wind had blown a branch across the drive. I stopped. I got out. There was an inch of water. I looked at the branch. It was big. Too big. I got back in the car. I placed the gear lever into low ratio and went off the drive and onto the grass in order to avoid the branch.

The Subaru did not like it.

It was wearing the wrong shoes. The wheels started to spin. For some reason I touched the window button. The window opened. There was a meteorological rumble interspersed with an electronic flute.

"Listen to that," I shouted.

Dr James cracked open her window. The wind lifted everything from off the dashboard. I snatched at the call sheet. It disappeared through the window. The wheels were spinning. The sounds outside seemed to be taking place in another dimension, an alien zone a few feet away was exploding. The wheels were spinning and the Subaru was digging itself into the mire until the beast found a grip on some kind of submerged solid. Aided by the hard mass it lifted itself like an artificial metal beast moving across a primeval bog. I fought the steering wheel making the animal charge the drive.

It jumped back onto the road.

Moving once again on the tarmac drive we could both hear wood being torn, it was being ripped from the tree behind us by a knife-like wind and we could see the evidence overtaking us. Small branches moving faster than our car!

Safely inside our tin box our attention was caught by something distant yet quite audible. It was a strange, rending sound as if a huge piece of paper had been violently ripped in two. I slowed. I looked in the rear view mirror. The brake lights lit the forest. I saw it in happening in slow motion. I stamped on the accelerator. The boxer engine pushed us back into our seats. I held on the steering wheel.

Dr James screamed at the top of her voice,

"What do think you are doing!"

"The tree behind us," I shouted.

And the car's transmission was whining and the rev counter was past the red zone, but I continued hanging onto the steering wheel like grim death because the sky was falling down.

"It was a near miss," I said as I slowed, trying to be calm.

But my pulse was in the red zone.

"I do not want near misses," Dr James said.

And her pulse was in the red zone.

I stopped the car. I got out. I shone the halogen spot. The white beam was like a spotlight. Through the sheets of rain it picked out a tree lying down. Blown over. My glasses were wet. I got back in the car. Closed the door. Reached for a tissue. Cleaned my glasses and then I turned and looked through the rear window. Black, it was black. I looked at Dr James. I saw the reflected lights from the dashboard in her glasses. She reached out as if to touch me. I broke out in a cold sweat.

"Close your window," Dr James said as she closed hers.

My window wound itself up until it automatically stopped. The sounds outside dropped a couple of octaves.

My hands were shaking.

"Are you all right?" my doctor asked.

"Are you?" I replied.

"No," she said.

"Well then," I said.

"It only just missed us," she said.

"If it had hit us then they would believe us," I said.

"Who?" my doctor asked.

"No one believes in near misses," I said.

"But it almost did hit us," my doctor said.

"A few seconds. A few seconds-adieu," I said.

"If we had not left those people in the car then we would not have had a near miss."

And she was right. And I said nothing. We sat in the car. The engine was running. The lights were on. It was raining. I was shaking. My doctor was shaking. I looked in the rear-view mirror. There was nothing. Black it was black. I wanted to get out and have a look. It was raining. I pushed the clutch in. selected first. I let the clutch out and moved further up the drive.

Eventually we arrived at a gated compound. It was a visitor centre. Everything was locked. Plastic chairs and tables had been blown right across the compound until a wire fence had abruptly stopped their journey. As the wind passed through the fence it transformed the structure into a self-generating musical instrument.

The fence was making an out of focus wail.

"We have to go back," my doctor said.

"We can't go back," I said, "not the way we came, there's a tree right across the road."

"If there's an east gate then there must be a west gate," my doctor said, "All roads lead to here, to this car park."

My doctor's logic was correct.

I drove around the car park and found another drive. It went through a forest. Branches littered the surface of the road. They snapped. We moved slowly. My doctor held onto the handle above her head.

"They were crazy about trees, there's a forest each side of the road," my doctor said.

"It's the hunting forest," I said, "the Normans covered half the surface of the land with them. They had Forest Laws. If a chap like me so much as made a deer pant he would be flayed alive. If a starving peasant caught a rabbit he would be hung. Later, after Captain Cook discovered Australia poachers were transported and that was a fate worse than death, almost like being sent to the moon, because there was no way back."

"Were they convicts or criminals?" my doctor asked.

"Convicts," I said," the criminals sent them there."

"I think that's the driveway the Earl told you about," my doctor said.

"There's a cattle grid," I said. It rattled as we drove over it.

"He never mentioned a cattle grid," my doctor said.

Our halogen headlights illuminated the track. Nothing had been over it for months. The grass was long. The track slowly turned right. We both saw the lodge. It was built 30 years into the reign of mad King George the Third. I switched the spots on. The heavy rain had filled the yard with water. Parked in front of the stables were four cars. An old Rover 3.5 litre coupe, its bonnet was raised. There was a tree as thick as a man's wrist growing up and through the engine compartment. Next to it, nettles surrounded the first Range Rover ever made. Briars covered what looked like a rotted canvas-bodied Land Rover. Parked in front of the back door was a four-door Range Rover. It was in use. There was an old Humber Super Snipe sitting in a garage with a broken door. It looked immaculate. I wondered what was behind the other closed and locked doors.

The Earl purchased a new car every 10 years and then dumped them. The modern ones.

I knew there were others.

I applied the handbrake. The rain looked like silver stair rods.

Dr James and I watched the rods telescope and turn to liquid on the bonnet of our car.

We looked at each other. We waited.

And then the apparition appeared.

A man standing holding a hurricane lamp materialized. He held a real old fashioned hurricane lamp with a wick burning and what was more he was holding it above his head and the wick was moving because of the wind and in his left hand the man held an umbrella which had turned inside out. He just stood there outside my driver's door and he looked at me and I looked at him through the glass and he lowered his hurricane lamp and he gestured for me to open my window, he made a revolving movement and the hurricane lamp moved in a semi-circle and the stair rods of rain hit the man and water was running off him as if he was in a shower and all the time the umbrella was losing its fabric piece by piece but still he held tightly to its hooked handle.

As the electric motor cracked my window the man started to talk and gesture towards the house.

"Are you the doctor?" he asked and he thrust his head towards me. It came at me. He managed to get his head inside the car. He shook his head. It was a skull holding a great mop of sodden yellow hair.

Boris Johnson had a brother.

Water fell from his hair. He shook his head again just like a dog does when it comes out of a river and then after another good shake he removed his head from inside the car and turned towards the house.

"She's up there," he shouted pointing towards a window on the flank end of the house, "she's being ill, she has no diazepam left, she's run out of it!"

"You never mentioned the cattle grid," I said.

"No," the man said, "I knew that you would miss it, everyone does."

I looked at Dr James and Dr James looked at me.

I hit the window button. The window closed.

"The show has begun," I said, "It could last for three acts but I will miss two of them, I'll wait here."

"You go up, he thinks you are the doctor," Dr James said as she opened the rear door to retrieve her bag.

I watched my doctor walk through the flooded yard and I wondered whether or not it really was the Earl she was walking with who was holding an inside out umbrella above her head.

Neither phone was able to transmit or receive. The car radio could only pick intermittent signals from the web of memories hanging in the electrolysed air. I left the engine running. I saw lights appear in windows. I saw the raindrops fall into the waterlogged yard. I saw waterfalls of water overflowing from the gutters. I wanted to tell someone about the tree.

I sat in the Subaru waiting.

And then the apparition appeared again. The Earl was standing there in the rain staring at me. He was crouched looking at me. I opened the window just enough to ask him what he wanted but not enough to allow his head inside.

"Do you do this often?" he asked.

"What?" I replied.

"Chauffeur to the doctor," he said.

And I noticed the way he rolled each word around in his mouth before he spat it out. He distorted the words and I imagined how it must have been at the court of the mad king George who could hardly speak a word of English and all the courtiers aping him so as to humour him.

"Only out of hours," I said. Imitating his accent.

"Ah," he said. And it was an aristocratic, mad Ahhh.

"You must know the area well," he said.

"Well enough," I said.

"Do you know the Bog?" he said.

"I was up there last year," I said.

"Strange place."

"Car started to move, it rocked by itself and I was sitting in it waiting," I said.

"Davis, Ron Davis," he said.

I looked at the man who was standing there in the rain, because it was pouring down, it was running down his face and it was as if he was completely unaware of it.

"Heart attack, died last year," he said.

"That's right," I said, "and the car moved, it started to rock."

"Could have been a Gnome," he said.

"It was a boar," I said.

"My great great great grandfather said that the little people were common enough in 1796, and my grandmother saw three as recently as 1927, they were crossing the Bog in broad daylight," he said.

"It was a boar, an old boar rubbing himself against the car," I said.

"In our employ for generations," he said.

"Who?" I said.

"Davis, grandfather like son, generation after generation all in our employ, daughter went to Cardiff university, end of an era, good stock, damn good stock and gone," he said swinging his hurricane lamp.

"Are you the Earl?" I asked.

"Indeed," he replied.

"Then you must be a descendant of the great Owain Glyn Dwr who beat Edmund Mortimer at the battle of Pilleth Hill in 1402," I said.

"Are you an historian?" the Earl replied.

"No," I said, "but I gleaned the information from the church at Pilleth whilst watching the vintage car club hill climb a few years ago."

"Good sport, you know," he said.

And the Earl made a face, he screwed his cheeks a little and the rain ran down his face and he swung his hurricane lamp and he wiped away a great drop of water from his chin.

"Improves the breed, dew know," he said.

"Oh," I said.

"Yes," he said, "that was the object of the exercise, trouble is there's never been a better car made than the 1932 Invicta S-type, anyway what dew know about it?"

"Got a Meadows engine, won Le Mans in 1928," I said.

"Lagonda, was a Lagonda, yes, yes, yes," the Earl said and the rain was running down his face and there was hardly any fabric left on his umbrella and the Earl held his hurricane lantern above his head.

"Donald Healey engineered the 100 mph chassis," I said.

"In 1930," the Earl said.

"Would never get one up Pilleth Hill," I said.

"Wheelbase too long, would struggle," the Earl said.

"Like Mortimer," I said.

"His own archers turned on him," the Earl said.

"Halfway up," I said.

"One thousand dead," The Earl said.

"And then the Welsh women cut off the private parts of the dead English," I said.

"And shoved them in their mouths," the Earl said.

"And the English government would not pay the ransom," I said.

"Idiots," the Earl said.

"So Mortimer married Owain's daughter," I said.

"Lost his name," the Earl said.

"Because the Welsh were matriarchal and the Normans were patriarchal," I said.

"And then we came back," the Earl said.

"The Tudors," I said.

There was a pause and then the Earl looked up into the heavens and the rain washed his face and he took a deep breath and he looked for a moment like a mad druid standing on a mountain in the rain and he started to shout,

"The noble Mortimer, leading the men of Herefordshire to fight, against the wild irregular Glendower, was by the rude hand of that Welshman taken and a thousand of his people butchered."

"William Shakespeare," I said, *"Henry IV."*

"I like you," the Earl said. "Come. Come. Come."

And so I followed a completely barmy baron across a flooded, Georgian backyard in torrential rain, lifting my feet like a horse taking part in a dressage event.

We went past a kitchen with a giant waste bin full of

empty Tesco baked bean cans. We went along a corridor, until we were inside an entrance hall. I saw the front door. I saw a great Fred Astaire stairway designed for ladies in low-cut ball gowns.

The door was massive.

The Adams family.

And ...

I was led into a room large enough to hold a full size tennis court.

The Earl reached for a light switch.

The chandelier was cut glass.

It illuminated the room like stars in the Milky Way.

Beneath it right in the centre of the room standing on a Persian carpet was a white Invicta S-Type.

The Earl held his hand over the top of his hurricane lamp and blew the wick. The lamp went out. There was a smell of burnt paraffin.

"1932, top speed 100 mph," the Earl said,

"In-line six.

Capacity 4467 cc.

Track, 4 ft 8 ins front and rear.

Wheelbase, 9 ft 10 ins."

The Earl looked at me and I looked at him and I tried to understand how it was that his ancestors came over with the Bastard King in 1066 and took the land from the Saxons and then made the world's very first account book, called Doomsday and ruled without a break for over a thousand years and still rule.

I tried to figure it out and came to the conclusion that it didn't matter anyway.

"You're right," he said, "never got it up Pilleth, threw it up Shelsley Walsh once, bloody handful, had to make suitable allowances, and would you like to hear it?"

I had no idea what he meant.

Was he going to start the thing up?

"How did you get it in here?" I asked.

He pointed toward the French windows.

I saw a pair of wooden ramps outside.

He walked around the white beast.

In front of a wall of bookshelves, in each corner stood a pair of Quad electrostatic loud speakers. They were wired to a Quad amp and pre amp. There was a turntable and a Ferrograph reel-to-reel tape recorder.

This was state of the art equipment in 1959.

In many respects it has never been improved.

The Earl reached for the mains plug. He switched on the juice. He twisted a dial. He turned the tape recorder on. A green light on the deck became illuminated. The Earl waited a few moments. The Earl started the tape deck. The reels moved. The Earl lifted his right hand. He threw his arm down.

The room became filled with an ocean of sound.

A wave burst into the room like a bottle of champagne exploding.

I could smell the rubber burning.

It was the start of a hill climb! And the mesh covers on the headlights of the car started to vibrate as the electrostatic loudspeakers released the active percussion trapped on the recording tape. It was the harmony of exploding pistons and screaming tyres and we were at Shelsley Walsh hill climb and the car disappeared up the hill and there was the rumbling noise of another car approaching the start.

And then the door opened and a woman walked in.

She walked across the room.

She bent over and pulled the electric plug out of its socket. It fell to the floor. The sounds coming from the speakers slowed and then stopped dead.

"I haven't finished being ill yet," she shouted.

She was wearing a nightdress.

It was silk.

It was short.

Her knickers were a pink thong.

The dress just covered her breasts.

Two thin straps ran over her shoulders.

There was an excitement in the straps.

When she left the room she closed the door with all the force she possessed.

"She was the last debutante," the Earl said.

He was standing in a puddle of water.

I was standing in a smaller puddle.

It was the only thing that made us equal.

7   The Green Man

IT'S RIGHT IN THE MIDDLE of flaming June, almost the longest day and the sky is leaking. Not only that but I'm taking my doctor to see a patient who has been living wild in Hazel Coppice, part of Mortimer Forest, where Wild Edric lived a thousand years ago as an outlaw because the Normans stole his land.

The patient who needs to be seen has not had his land stolen; he has just lost his sanity.

Skunk.

Dope.

Crack.

He thinks he is the green man who has seen God sitting under an oak tree.

His brother waits for him to fall asleep and then hits him on the head with a rubber-headed hammer.

The brother is on heroin.

The father is on the parish council.

The mother is in the Women's Institute and makes jam.

So. I am driving in the rain towards an exploding crisis in a 4x4 car equipped with the very latest electronic gear, unbreakable laptop, printer, mobile phones and a GPS device controlled by satellite signals from radios inside artificial asteroids moving 100 miles above the earth's surface.

Six satellites track me.

The dispatchers inside the control centre look at a giant plasma screen. They know where every car in the zone is.

I am tagged.

Without this equipment nobody in the organisation knows where anyone is. The dispatchers are so used to using this gear that when they leave work they immediately hold their personal mobile phone to the side of their face and inform another that they have just left work. The transferring to others of this knowledge comforts them somewhat and eases the voyage home.

None of this high-tech gear will help the green man. Nothing we have inside the car will stop the green man's brother from beating seven shades of shit out of him once he falls asleep. In fact when we arrive at the house the sight of the car with its chequered painted sides will probably send the whole family into a permanent freak-out.

In 1188 Gerald of Wales set out from Hereford on a journey round Wales. This remarkable trip was made without a GPS device or any kind of road map. He knew where he was on the face of the earth. He made the last part of his journey from Shrewsbury to Hereford via Wenlock Edge, Bromfield Priory and then Ludlow Castle and on to Leominster in three days.

He was on foot. He walked.

If Gerald, on his travels round Wales with Archbishop Baldwin, had encountered a man who had seen God sitting beneath an oak tree, the Archbishop would have made the man a saint.

The society we now live in will section him.

The society we now live in will fry his brain with electricity or drugs.

The society we now live in does not believe in God.

Without a GPS device 21st century man has no idea where he is or where he is going.

Fact: all GPS devices are directed from heaven.

In the distance the battleship grey sky opened up and slanting rays of russet and gold sunlight play across the landscape, spotlighting an old rusted corrugated barn.

The windscreen wipers remove the last spots of rain,

enabling me to see better this palette of nature's harmonious perfection.

I have a vague idea when this old barn, leaving the peripherals of my vision, was built. It would have been constructed at that time in our history when the Industrial Revolution was in full pelt.

Climate change started in 1886.

It was the steam engine. It made horses bolt. The steam and smoke made it rain. It rained so much back then that wheat ears rotted on their stalks.

Mildew. Crops turned black. Rivers burst.

The Great Flood. You can see the mark on the Bread Walk.

It rained for 10 years.

Climate change started in 1886.

But funnily enough the price of corn went down.

This was because McCormack had invented the reaper. In two years thousands of the things were tied to Shire horses and each one did the work of a dozen men. The great prairies of Canada and America were opening up. Steam trains carried corn to the eastern seaboard. Steamships sailed into Liverpool loaded with North American surplus corn. Corn exchanges were set up. They were the first modern commodity markets.

North America became the breadbasket of the world. It was the beginning of cheap food and there was nothing the British farmer could do about it except grow beef.

Corn down, horn up.

Cows need winter feed and so the corrugated steel barn was built.

As the rusty old barn disappeared I thought about others who crossed the Atlantic more than 150 years ago.

The steamships bringing the corn into Liverpool would not have gone back to America empty. Although there were no radios or televisions back then people somehow knew that England produced the best beef.

Visitors to the Philadelphia Centennial Exhibition in 1877

saw Hereford cattle paraded in the sawdust ring. Americans liked what they saw. England was a green wetland producing fine long succulent grass. Hereford cattle love grass.

Herefords convert grass into steaks.

Protein.

Red meat puts lead in yer pencil.

The farmers in Herefordshire villages like Wigmore and Pembridge had been producing the best beef in the world since 1723. In 1881, the bull, Anxiety, born in Stocktonbury, near Leominster, was exported to the United States.

In 1882, 152 Herefords were shipped to America from Liverpool.

These were the cattle John Wayne lassoed on the silver screen.

Beautiful white-faced Herefords.

I had a conversation about it with Jeff James whilst drinking beer in the Wheatsheaf. His sister keeps a history of the James family. It goes back two or three hundred years. One of the ancestors called Tom, who was the second of seven brothers, became a stockman. He was born in 1847 and knew more about the Hereford herd than any one else. So much so that he was in great demand as an authority on the breed. Most importantly he was an expert on the insemination of the species and there was no artificial insemination in those days.

They used the real thing: Hereford bulls, with rings in their noses.

It has been calculated by medical experts that there are more than a million live fishes in one ejaculation of human sperm.

One can therefore only imagine how much seed there is in a bull's massive ball sack.

Now what we are talking about is big money.

REAL BIG MONEY.

In 1884 the Hereford bull Lord Wilton was sold for £3,990. Back then you could buy a country estate for that. Right up until 1965 you could buy a house anywhere in this country for that amount of wonga. Cattle, was, is and always will be big money.

In 1898 Tom James bought 12 Hereford bull calves from Hereford market and drove them up the A49 through Ludlow over the Wenlock edge, via Shrewsbury and on across north Shropshire and Cheshire.

When the herd arrived at the Mersey it moved along the banks of that river until it came to the new Albert Docks In the Mersey estuary.

Once he arrived at the Albert Docks Tom James found a ship going to America. Not only that but Mr James went with his herd all the way to Boston. There he disembarked and drove the herd out and on across America until he reached Kansas.

He started off with adolescent bull calves. By the time he arrived in the Wild West his bull calves were grown up and randy. The inseminator then put them to mate with Texas Longhorns and the result was a near perfect breed well suited for the environment the animals were to live in.

About the same time in our history as the inseminator Tom James was touring America, others were moving out of the Shropshire Hills and crossing the Atlantic Ocean.

These were coal miners.

After the first steam digger started to work on the side of Clee Hill a thousand men were made redundant.

The unemployed miners who once worked on the Bonk would have probably heard about the need for miners in the Appalachian Mountains.

More than likely Tom James spread the news.

"There's work out there if you wants it."

Perhaps the news was heard in a pub like the Nelson where a couple of ex miners sang and bowed a violin for beer.

They had no alternative other than to beg and slowly starve if they stayed here. Better to busk their way to Liverpool, they had nothing to lose.

You can only imagine what it felt like as they slept under a hedge somewhere at the side of the A49, dreams turning into nightmares because they would never ever see the land that was once home ever again.

They were economic refugees but unlike today there were no passports, no visas, no finger-printed identity cards or electronic scanning machines, they had nothing to declare except themselves and that they were diggers, miners and all miners have good common sense because you ain't gonna survive long underground without it, and America needed as many humans as it could get with those qualifications.

So they went north.

They had no maps.

But they knew where the sun was.

Perhaps a year later they were underground, mining coal.

When they were not mining coal they sang songs about remembered things and the one who could bow a violin was always in demand. And so there were Clee Hill miners in the Blue Grass mountains and their music became Hillbilly music and it was all about heartbreak, loss, cheating, loss and more loss and then it armed itself with banjos, harmonicas, drop-tuned guitars, washboards and it became Country-folk and Bluegrass.

Country and Western roots came from Clee Hill.

"It was seldom accompanied with drums," I said, thinking out loud.

"What are you talking about?" said Dr Downs.

"Country music, like Appalachian and Bluegrass," I said.

Dr Downs shook his head. Dr Downs looked at the call sheet.

"It was born on Clee Hill," I said.

Dr Downs continued looking at the call sheet.

"He's going back to Shelton," he said.

I drove up a gravelled drive.

It had stopped raining.

The yard was large enough to have a *Manneken Pis* statue in the centre.

It was pissing through a stone penis.

Dr Downs knocked the door of the Victorian house.

Dr Downs went inside.

I saw wide views and a trout stream.

Dr Downs came out. He waved for me to go in.

The green man was standing in the kitchen. He was holding on to a mug of coffee. On the side of the mug was an orange label. It said "CHAOS, PANIC and DISORDER. My work here is done."

The mother and father were sitting together on a brown leather sofa in the front room. A television flickered.

The green man was wearing a Barbour wax cotton jacket. It was green. Moss green. There was green moss in his long hair. His face was green stubble. He stank. An old billy goat smells sweeter. He wore thick glasses. His face was all blackheads, craters and lines; it looked like the surface of the moon.

The green man turned towards me and walked out of the kitchen and stood waiting in the porch. Dr Downs made the 'follow and keep an eye on him' gesture with his eyes.

The green man walked across the yard. He opened the side door of a large wooden garage. I followed him inside. There was one large window. On the back wall were shelves. There were tinplate railway lines on the shelves. Three clockwork Hornby engines coupled up to trucks and coaches were on the rails. In the corner was a wine rack. The green man pulled a bottle of Cotes du Rhone wine from the rack. He looked at it. There was nothing to open it. He replaced it. He searched for a screw top bottle. He found Tesco *vin ordinaire*.

He drank.

Stray droplets clung to his chin.

"What it means is a piece of the pie," he said, "just one small slice, a sliver, out of the total reality. Do you smoke, gimme a fag, please."

I reached into my jacket pocket. I pulled out a packet of French cigarettes, *Gitanes*. I offered him one.

"I have been to Paris," he said.

We smoked.

"I was in the music business," he said, "Atlantic Records, musicians want things. They got habits. They can't give up. I scored dope. It's all over," he said.

History.

"Now they try to get me through the television. The government control the media. I know. I been there."

I saw the filth on his face start to run like melting wax.

"I don't want to cry. It's just my face is wet," he said.

We smoked.

His eyes behind his glasses would not stop leaking. He reached into his pocket and dabbed at his face with a handkerchief the colour of dried brown putty.

"They control the brain, they control yer feelings, television is a tap of shit, I'm homeless, and those are my trains. I'm embargoed from home, I'm a fucking refugee," he said. "They are after me."

We smoked.

We waited. Dr Downs came in. I left.

I sat in the car. Dr Downs came out. He was going in. Voluntary.

The ambulance came. The green man got in. His mother and father sat watching the television in the front room.

There had been no sign of the brother.

The green man was going off in an ambulance. He was going to face bigger nightmares than a couple of unemployed miners who took country music to the U.S.A. in 1889.

Hard labour kept the miners sane.

I slowed when I saw the pheasant.

It went under the car.

I stopped.

Dr Downs got out.

The bird was not dead.

Its wing was broken.

Dr Downs expertly wrang the bird's neck.

I opened the boot.

I dropped it behind the drug box.

Dr Downs is not a vegetarian.

Forty-five minutes later I drove into a farmyard on that side of the Clee Hill slope that ends in Tenbury and is called Nash.

When Dr Downs came out of the farmhouse with the farmer I sensed that he would need some drugs.

Together the three of us approached the car. I opened the boot and the pheasant flew up, like a jack-in-the-box, up he went and then he flew right across the farmyard over a hedge and into a field of corn.

"Them are a hard bird," the farmer said. "You thinks you killed 'em and you only knocks 'em out. You wants ta wring their neck afor you puts 'em in the car."

"I did," Dr Downs said.

"You did'na do it properly then," the farmer said.

It was laid down behind the drug box like a dead glove

And it rose up like a fist

On the end of a spring in a box

And it startled the sparrows in the hedge

And pheasants do not sing

They emit sound

And it emitted its sound

As it flew over the hedge

On one wing.

8   *Keep Running After a Mad Dog*

SHIT HAPPENS, FADES AWAY and no one tells it. And I wonder what happened to the young ones who had been taken into care on that first day of summertime.

I am what I am and the poor girl did not want to be what she was any more.

Most humans live long lives that end in a hospital bed.

The end will be a struggle against death helped by a medical priesthood.

It will not make a blind bit of difference.

When our time is up it is up.

We will all end up as a stone slab with a name on it in a graveyard and if we are lucky we will leave behind two or three people, a wife, brother or sister to still bear the light, the legend, in their heads for a few more years until they too die and all that is left is an old black and white film which becomes an out of focus aura of a vague face to our grandchildren.

And that's all there is to it.

That's life.

But we live in a land of plenty and too many dump their children before the sell by date.

We have everything and nothing.

It was the first evening of the first day of summertime.

The road was passing beneath the car. The day was one hour longer. It was a different flow of time. There was a different smell in the air. The light was another consistency. Summertime. Spring's spurt of vitality.

Not the right time to want to hang yourself.

It was dusk. I pressed a button on the dash.

The road moving underneath the car like a conveyor belt became illuminated by two powerful white lights.

Blue tinted halogen spotlights.

It was not yet dark enough to see the plasma of space. At this time yesterday it was completely dark. Another hour would have to pass before the night sky laid bare its construction.

A thousand years ago prince poets would have ridden up this valley on proud horses after a raid on the Severn border. They would have sheathed their swords and counted the stolen cattle here because this was where it was safe to do so. Then there was no such thing as summer time. Back then 16-year-old girls did not try to hang themselves. No, they would have been promised or already married because that would have been their lot.

There was no choice.

There was not that luxury.

They would cement relationships with each other's tribe.

They could not afford to go mad.

My doctor is called Pyke, David Pyke. He is newly qualified. He wants to be a GP in a rural practice. He applies for jobs. He attends interviews. He keeps looking at the call sheet. I can see from the expression on his face that he is submerged in the madness of the call.

We are moving toward it.

I know where I am going.

I made a call to the home.

The person who answered did not know how to direct me to the home.

She handed me over to someone who was local.

The unqualified cleaner.

And I wondered how on earth people could work on the side of a mountain miles away from anywhere without knowing where they were.

"The road to the coast," she said, "opposite the large layby. The one with the portaloo toilet. One mile up a narrow hawthorn hedged lane and then over two cattle grids. Mobile phones do not work up here."

I had the information.

I found the hedged lane, green hawthorn shoots smothered in the furry dusk of evening.

Both of us looked at the expanding shadows in the folds of the Welsh hills expecting to see at the end of the road, 'Stone Hall Manor Farm' once the home of a Welsh noble who had Tudor blood.

When we saw it, it looked like something out of *The Wind in the Willows*. Toad would have lived in it. Toad would have loved it.

One hundred years ago there would have been cattle, sheep, pigs, hens, a rooster, ducks in the duck pond, doves in the dovecote, a great midden and border collies would have already been alerted to our imminent arrival. They would have smelt us a mile away.

Instead we came upon a sterile car park covered in pea gravel.

There was a Toyota Hi-Lux four door next to a great Nissan pick-up with dark windows, a film star's Range Rover with dark windows, two Vauxhall Corsa two door saloons, a Citroen C1, a Ford Escort and a white Merc nine-seater people carrier with dark windows. All the metal beasts were tethered to a white painted wooden fence enclosing a series of horse jumps, oil drums painted red and white.

Behind it all six horses grazed in a ten-acre field. The horses wore blankets.

They were not tethered.

"It's a riding school," Dr Pyke said.

"No," I said, "it's a special needs home, it has to be the right place, and I followed the directions."

"Therapeutic, they use the horses as part of the healing process," Dr Pyke said.

"The horse whisperer," I said.

"No not exactly, but something like that. The horse whispers to the human, some think it's a healing process," Dr Pyke said.

As we rumbled over the cattle grid all the lights came on at once, giving the impression that we had arrived at an open prison.

"Therapy," I said, "therapy, horse therapy, it helps the nutters."

"You can't say that," Dr Pyke said.

When all the lights came on not only did it illuminate the yard but it also illuminated the field. As I swung the car around the gravel yard it made a long wave of crunching sounds like a tide receding. The horses lifted their heads. The horses swung their tails. I cracked the window. The gravel settled into another position.

"You enjoyed that," Dr Pyke said.

"The door has opened, they're expecting us," I said.

"We come in peace," Dr Pyke said.

"Reality is too harsh," I said.

The doctor lifted his bag off the rear seat. The doctor draped his stethoscope around his neck.

It was his badge. He was young.

One minute after my doctor went into the restored manor in the Tudor style the lights went out. It was 9.10 on the Orange phone and there was no signal. It was one minute past nine on the T-phone and there was no signal. I was totally isolated.

Dispatch would not know where we were.

I laughed.

I looked at the entrance, I saw the great door. Six steps up. I looked at the hinges on the great door and at the tower with the narrow windows. A fortified manor house. It gave the building a sinister feeling. King Arthur could have lived in it. There would be room enough for a round table where all the knights would sit. There would be no problems of precedence. All the knights would be equal. You could use it for a film set.

Camelot.

Star Wars.

I wondered about the 16-year-old girl inside who wanted to hang herself.

I waited and nothing happened.

I thought about the cry for help from a creature miles away from anywhere, isolated on the side of a mountain protected by carers who have no idea where they are. But, I thought, there is method in their madness. This place is a drying-out zone for users of mobile phones, why else would they send anyone up here? I am on the phone. I am on the train. I am in Tesco's. I am at the skate park. I am outside college. I am in the car. I am coming back from Jack's.

I send text messages night and day.

Not anymore you don't.

I waited.

I looked at the horses. Three of them were standing motionless. I wondered if the beasts really slept standing up.

I waited and nothing happened. Not even the radio worked. The preset button for the Third Programme selected a Welsh station. I wondered about it, perhaps there is a very sophisticated way of changing the language as you move over the border.

I leaned forward to see if the clouds had moved so that I might see the stars and the labyrinth of the night.

Thick cloud.

I was born 25 miles from here. Only 15 from the Welsh border and yet I don't speak a word of Welsh. I speak French fluently, Italian, with difficulty, and I can find my way around Greek. And no one inside the old manor will speak Welsh except, maybe the cleaner because everyone here does not belong here or want to be here. The vibrations tell me so. I have no need of any kind of modern device to explain the feelings.

And then the lights came on, all of them and at once.

I looked at the door. My doctor was talking to a man. The man's hair was long. It was plaited. He had a two-foot long pigtail. When the man turned the pigtail swung. I imagined him sitting like my sister used to so that my mother could plait her hair. Unless it was an extension? Perhaps he clipped it on like a bow tie.

He walked with the doctor towards the car. He was explaining something. The tattoo on his right arm was as complicated as a stained glass window. I wanted to pull his pigtail. If he ever worked on a building site somebody would pull his pigtail. He would never work on a building site because he would not know the difference between a bag of cement and a brick.

"Let's go," Dr Pyke said before he'd shut his door.

"The phones don't work," I said.

"I've done all the phoning," Dr Pyke said.

"I mean I can't tell Dispatch where we are," I said.

"Let's get out of here," Dr Pyke said.

When we passed over the second cattle grid my doctor looked at me and I looked at him.

I asked him how the girl was.

"She was alright," he replied.

"Oh," I said.

"But there was a 20-year-old who knelt on the floor and just banged his head."

"What did you do?" I asked.

"Nothing, waited for him to stop," the doctor said. "The whole thing is shattered, what's the point of giving chemical drugs after plant psychedelics, it's falling apart, they are all from inner cities, it's alienation. I can't figure out what's going on, we've had a hundred years of psychotherapy and the world's getting worse."

"I have to make the call," I said looking at the phone, "we got five bars here."

"It's called no-mob-phobia," the doctor said.

"What?" I said.

"It's half the problem."

"What?" I said.

"Their mobiles don't work, they feel isolated, abandoned," the doctor said.

" I was thinking about that when you were inside."

I stopped in a lay-by. I made my call. The dispatcher wanted to know why we had not made contact. I asked her why she had not tried to make contact. When she said that she couldn't I laughed and said Wales. She then wanted the time of arrival and the time of departure. The dispatcher also told us that we had a patient waiting in the MIU.

Dr Pyke reached behind him for the Rugged laptop.

"A nine-year-old with asthma," he said.

As we pulled back onto the main road, full moonbeams dissolved the clouds.

"A full moon doesn't help," I said.

My doctor nodded his head as we moved further away from the dark whirlpool of the absurd.

Because both doctors and drivers work out of hours during the time when others lie watching the plasma screen like cows chewing the cud, doctor and driver sometimes abandon themselves to the delights of the yawning, a yawning crossing the borders of sensuous pleasure, leading sometimes to a painful cramp of the palate, almost to nausea.

We both finished our yawning as we approached the bridge over the river Teme at Leintwardine. It was there right on the bridge with the water running under us when my doctor asked me who the nurse was in MIU.

"Big Sal," I replied.

I knew what the doctor was getting at.

"She will have done the obs and maybe started the nebulizer," I said. "Not only that, if she thinks it necessary she will phone for a blue light, it could be that the patient will be gone before we even get there."

"I'm happy with that," Dr Pyke said.

They were in the waiting room and we had to pass them. As we passed the little girl started to wheeze. This was an automatic reaction to a doctor's presence. A patient will always cough or wheeze as he or she opens the door to the consultation room. It is an unconscious reaction in order to prove that they are ill, the louder the cough the stronger the cough mixture!

Whilst my doctor was seeing the little girl I started doing a drug check.

Fifteen minutes later Dr Pyke came into the room looking for a box of steroids.

"When the level of tolerance for discomfort or pain has been lowered by the medicalization of life then we give them what they want," he said.

"That's what Dr Watson would have said," I said.

"I was a registrar at his practice," Dr Pyke said.

Twenty minutes later a people-carrier arrived from the leisure centre with a 15-stone giant who had dislocated his shoulder whilst playing five-a-side football on a wooden floor. He walked sideways like a crab. His arm hung at a very unnatural angle.

The nurse in MIU would see him first. Big Sal would clerk him in and then she would phone our Dispatch and create a call for my doctor.

I knew what would happen next. What would happen would be that Dr Pyke, because he was not long out of Wolverhampton Accident and Emergency, would give him some diazepam, and then attempt to put the arm back together. This is what young doctors like to do. The older perhaps wiser doctors would send him up the road.

As sure as eggs are eggs, 25 minutes later I was in MIU pulling on a towel, which was threaded under the patient's armpit, whose shoulder was well and truly dislocated.

Dr Pyke was pushing his arm trying to place the ball into the socket.

"Pull," he shouted.

"I am," I shouted back.

It did not happen.

"It's just like putting a button into a buttonhole," Dr Pyke explained, "let's try again."

I was sweating. I had my jacket off. I tried to visualise the buttonhole. The patient did not want to go to Hereford. He wanted it over. He wanted his arm back in place. He wanted to go to work in the morning. He liked to lift weights and had got knots of muscles in his belly that looked as if they would pop as he thrashed about on the bed.

The giant was still taking short breaths. Dr Pyke waited until his breathing returned to somewhere near normal.

"We are going to try again," Dr Pyke told him. "Look if you want we'll call it a day."

"Put it in, gotta go in, put it in, put it back in please, it's happened before when I played rugby."

"You didn't tell me that," Dr Pyke said.

"Twice, just don't mind if I shout," the patient said..

"Listen," I said. "If I pull any harder then he comes off the bed."

"Hold his legs, nurse," Dr Pyke said.

And so Big Sal held his legs.

And we started all over again and I was pulling both ends of a towel and the doctor was pushing whilst at the same time manoeuvring the upper arm and the rugby player was shouting for Jesus Christ to have mercy because of the grievous pain.

"You fucking bastards," he shouted and he shouted so loud that the sister on Dinham Ward came running down the corridor.

And I pulled and all the time prayed that the socket found the buttonhole. I imagined that because it had happened twice before then the hole which was like a buttonhole would be easily found by the ball on the end of the arm, get somewhere near it and it would go right in.

Then it happened: all of a sudden it went in. It went in.

It did and Dr Pyke was shouting "It's over," and the giant of a man who was also a rugby player was salivating and shouting "Fucking hell" whilst spreading spittle all over the place.

"It's all over," Dr Pyke said as he turned away rubbing his hands together.

And then there was an absolute period of elation and achievement and the big fellow's arm was no longer hanging, his arm was back in place. He was mended.

We had mended his arm!

He lifted it up.

And big Sal was laughing because she did not think it would happen.

And it was a good job there was nothing to drink. Had there been a bottle of whisky then I think, no I am sure, absolutely sure that we would have all ended up taking a shot for medicinal purposes you understand, just to alleviate the stress that had passed, as it were.

"Well, that's what you call doctoring," I said.

And Big Sal nodded.

And the giant got up off the bed.

"Good man," he said. And he shook the doctor's hand and he gripped and squeezed the doctor's hand, "Just seeing that it works," he said and the doctor pulled his hand away and shook it.

"It works," he said.

"It works," the rugby player said.

"All my work's got a six months' guarantee," Dr Pyke said.

"Take him up to the Church Inn," I said to his girlfriend, "all the others will be up there by now, good stiff drinkers, fine fellows and don't forget the old Ludlow saying:

Keep running after a mad dog and it will never bite you; drink always before the thirst and it will never come upon you!"

The rugby player nodded.

His woman shook her head.

"Don't encourage him, Sarge," she said.

9 Two Saracen Doctors

IN 1344 A SARACEN DOCTOR came to practice in our town. He was physician to Joan Mortimer who lived in the Castle.

He could have graduated from only one of three medical schools, Baghdad, Cairo, or more than likely Cordoba.

Best bet is Cordoba.

The Arabs of Spain brought the study of medicine to Europe in the 12th and 13th centuries.

More than 600 years later, I was driving another Saracen physician who had studied at Baghdad, through the south Shropshire countryside back to base in a Honda 4x4.

We were moving at speeds of between 40 and 60 miles an hour along twisting lanes with green hedges. The first Saracen could not have imagined that mankind would ever move at such a speed. Back then even news only travelled at never more than 50 miles a day. The second Saracen takes speed for granted. Not only is he able to fly anywhere he wants faster than swifts in the sky, he also drives an old MX5 sports car with a great deal of panache.

The only thing my Saracen and the first Saracen would have in common is the knowledge that the human body has 200 bones plus three in each ear. England and the rest of Europe were still floundering about in the Dark Ages, where ideas like eating pig dung for pleurisy were still in vogue. It was not until Vesalius had dissected executed convicts and then published the first definitive map of the body in 1543 that Europeans had any idea how the human body worked.

Up until then Baghdad, Cairo and Cordoba were the centres of science.

Just before the old railway station at Horderley I swerved to avoid six pheasants wandering along the road. They ran like aircraft taking off until enough speed or fear had been developed in their little bodies to facilitate take-off.

One by one they flew over the hedge whilst at the same time making the pheasant alarm call, which is a strange kind of cackling sound and caused my Saracen doctor to grab the handle over the door, lift himself up and look over the hedge where he saw the first bird land on the stubble left by combine harvesters after they had shaved the field.

Both of us saw the fields.

We saw that the surface of the earth was covered in a yellow fleece, which was like a giant eiderdown spread over an unmade bed.

It was the landscape after the harvest and there was a certain mellowness to everything. We saw the ripeness of the coming Fall. We saw the fruit trees laden with apples, pears and damsons. There was a wild harvest of blackberries. There were green sloes.

"Sloe gin," I said making a mental note of where the tree was.

"What do you mean?" the Saracen asked.

"You know what gin is don't you?" I said.

"Gin and tonic," he replied, "I like it."

"A gentleman's," I said.

"What do you mean?" he said.

"A double measure," I said.

"A gentleman's," he said, filing away another meaning for an English word in the temporal part of his brain where the memory of speech and words are contained.

Over the hedge there were nettles that were impenetrable clumps of stings spreading with thistles unchecked and in profusion.

"So why is it called slow?" asked the Saracen.

"It's the sloes. They are wild damsons, they are green now, but they will turn blue and are best after a frost. What you do is to pick them and place them in a large demijohn jar and cover them with sugar and then fill the jar with gin and you leave it until Christmas and then filter the liquid and then you can drink it. Preferably after Christmas dinner or any time in the evening."

"With tonic," he said.

"Only if you are stupid. Neat, you take it neat." I said.

"Neat," he said.

"Neat," I replied.

"Like a malt," he said.

"It's better than any kind of Scotch," I said.

"Even a very expensive one?" he said.

"Sloe gin is a perfect drink for a man or a woman," I said. "It makes a woman relax because it has an uplifting quality. It is best to administer it to a woman two hours before bed and then you will reap a reward force nine on the Carl Richter scale."

"Can you buy it?" asked the Saracen, his eyes lighting up.

"Yes," I said. "You can buy it, but bought sloe gin is weak, expensive and lacks clout. I will give you some, it will be the real thing."

The Saracen thanked me as we drove past an old blacksmith shop with steel stacked as if in an old refuse dump. Next to the dump under an old oak tree we saw an old iron bed with an old pushbike leaning against it.

Further down the road there was a brown horse looking over a five-barred gate with a clot of shining horse flies dancing between his ears illuminated by yellow rays from the setting sun.

We then passed a church with a lychgate. It was newly tiled and looked like the roof of a small house. And there were cottages surrounded by railings all submerged in the lushness of old fashioned country gardens like ideal happy snapshots from postcards of Olde Merrie England and the past.

We were moving down the Clun valley.

It is border country and happily contained because it is a countryside without wildness, even the hills in the distance with their symphony of colours, sometimes green and brown and sometimes grey and blue are not really wild.

"They still have Lords around here don't they?" the Saracen asked.

"They do," I replied.

"And Ladies and Squires and real Dukes," he said.

"They do," I said.

"They are called the aristocracy are they not?" he said.

"Correct," I said.

"And yet they have banned hunting," he said.

"Well not quite. It was not the aristocracy it was New Labour, they banned hunting and smoking, they are puritans like Cromwell was. If they could they would ban alcohol and dancing except on the television which is a tap of shit running 24 hours a day."

"What do you mean, not quite?" asked the Saracen.

"The country class and the aristocracy hunt the fox and then they call the hounds off and send up a bird of prey to kill the fox," I said.

"Ingenious," the Saracen said and he laughed.

"They are not stupid and that is why they are the ruling classes," I said.

We looked at the hills and saw sheep like white dots and old mine works with black stagnant ponds and conifer plantations and everything was all fenced in. The only way a human could experience it was to go hunting, jump hedges and five-barred gates on a horse or by car on little winding roads.

Which was what we were doing.

As we approached the village of Bromfield I decided to leave the A49 and take the left turn just before the Clive Arms. I wanted to show the Saracen doctor who was educated in Baghdad the tump or mound where the first Saracen doctor who practised in Ludlow in the 1300s removed the dragon.

"That's where it was," I said as I pulled the car to a stop in front of a mound with an old oak tree growing on its top.

"That is where the Saracen doctor removed the dragon in 1344. And it is all recorded in a medieval chronicle written by the historian Thomas of Walsingham."

"Why did he remove the dragon?" the Saracen asked.

"That's the interesting part about it," I said, "What the dragon was doing was guarding a hoard of gold.

"Now it could be that the Saracen invented the dragon so that he could take the gold because back then people who believed that eating pig dung was good for pleurisy also believed in dragons. He could have been operating some kind of con, which in the end went terribly wrong. He could have wanted to keep people away from the tump.

"What happened was this.

"The Saracen doctor went to the Lord of the manor, who was at that time an Earl called Warren and he asked him if he could remove a great serpent or dragon that was causing problems by eating sheep and generally committing great ravages right across the open land near Bromfield.

"Permission was given and so the Saracen went and removed the dragon by shouting incantations in Arabic down and into a great burrow that he had already dug.

"However Peter the Picard, a Lombard man living in a tent in the Old Gate Fee, heard about the Saracen and his apprentice walking out to the Broomfield with digging equipment he had borrowed from Sooty Pratt the blacksmith. They followed him at a distance hiding in the broom bushes. They heard his incantations and saw him and the apprentice digging.

"Now Peter the Picard was a Lombard man from Lombardy. He was well travelled and had heard an old poet tell the Anglo Saxon legend about dragons guarding gold. He remembered the last part of one long poem the old poet had told in a tavern in Ebbsfleet in the Thames estuary. The

Saxons and Angles were beer drinking and they shouted and laughed as the old poet performed.

"Half of the poem Picard could not understand but he remembered the last few words:

They that let the ground
Keep that ancestral treasure
Gold under gravel, gone to earth
Forever.

"And the soil under Bromfield was and still is all gravel.

"That fact about the gravel got on Picard's nerves. It all seemed to add up because the Saxons working the land for the Norman Lords in this part of the world would, after drinking beer talk about the treasure left by Wild Edric. They would tell of his exploits, of how he lived in exile outside the law because he would not swear allegiance to the Normans. They had stolen his land. All the land was his from Lydbury right past the Clee hills. Wild Edric would not accept Norman rule. The Normans called him Edric the Sauvage and he was such a bastard to them that he had to be killed three times. Each time the Normans killed him he would rise up again. He became supernatural. He would roam about like a ghost on a white horse.

"The third time the Normans killed Wild Edric they buried him under the lead mines right in the very centre of the Long Mynd.

"How the Saxons would love telling the story of Wild Edric. It was a saga and they would become silent when they told about the gold."

" 'Ah the gold,' they would whisper.

"And the more Picard the Lombard thought about it the more he was convinced that the Saracen had found the gold and was using the dragon as a pretext in order to keep the curious away.

"He was not afraid of a dragon. For the Lombard men dragons did not exist. They were not Saxons. They watched and waited and when the Saracen left the tump after the second dig, they took his shovels he'd left behind and they dug and found the gold, which was easy because the Saracen had already done most of the work.

"However, the retainers of the Earl had got wind of what was going on. They too were suspicious of the Saracen. They went out on horses after the Saracen had returned and they found Picard and his men hiding the treasure in broom bushes so that they could return later with horses and speed as far away from Ludlow as quickly as possible.

"It did not end as the Saracen had wanted but he must have wriggled his way out of a sticky situation because he received a golden cup as a reward and continued practicing medicine for the Mortimers until he died aged 89. Since he was a Muslim he was buried just outside the church gate but facing towards Mecca."

I reversed and moved away from the old tump with the oak tree on it and drove towards the town in silence until my Saracen asked where Walsingham was.

"Where?" I said,

"Walsingham, the town where Thomas the historian came from," my Saracen said.

"I don't know," I said, "somewhere in the East. Probably a small Saxon village where they went Wassailing, which is by the way an old Saxon festival that involves drinking large quantities of beer at about this time of year. In other words it was a well-organised form of binge drinking."

We pulled into our hospital just in time to see an ambulance arrive with a patient that my doctor would have to eventually clerk in.

On the side of the ambulance was the Maltese cross. It was a St John Ambulance Brigade ambulance.

I pointed to the cross and asked my Saracen doctor if he knew what it meant.

He did. He knew the history of the Knights of the Order of Saint John of Jerusalem.

I pointed to what was written in red letters under the door.

The Crusader it said.

The Saracen laughed.

"Keep that thing out of Walsall or Wolverhampton," he said. "The Muslims see that thing they'll burn it."

"I'll make tea," I said.

"Black, no sugar," the second Saracen said as he took a photo of the ambulance.

Half an hour later we looked out of the very top of the window of the consulting room and saw a red sky.

Red sky at night

Shepherd's delight

An autumn sunset.

As we marvelled at it there was panic at the side entry.

There were three of them and they were unable to read the instructions on the door telling them in large black capital letters what to do out of normal hours.

Bang, bang, bang, went the door and then they held onto the doorknob and started to rattle it.

I lifted the receiver.

"What is the problem?" I shouted down the intercom.

There was a pause.

"He's been shot," a female shouted.

Big Sal was working the MIU. I could hear her moving out to the side door.

I followed.

Sal opened the door.

There were three of them. Two guys who looked and moved like bouncers, no neck, one bald, the other stubble, shoulders hunched, arms curved out from the body like a pair of cowboys poised for the draw. Gym fanatics, iron pumpers, steroid milkshakes, rings in their ears.

The girl with them was about 16, in stilettos, with a pierced navel, tennis-ball tits and a goose-pimpled cleavage.

She was texting on a red mobile phone.

We were right back in the 21st century.

It was surreal. It was more than surreal.

Tweedledum and Tweedledee with Alice and you could not figure out what part Alice was playing or even if she should be there.

"He's been shot," said Alice, pointing at Tweedledum's thigh with her mobile phone.

After Alice had made her point she continued texting with great ferocity.

Tweedledum walked with a limp and he was hurting.

There was a hole in his trousers. There was blood and what looked like dead meat under the hole.

Tweedledee made a throat-tearing retching sound and then spat a stream of spit down the stairwell that leads down to the basement.

The three of them then moved like crippled crabs, a sideways motion. It was as if they were moving in sympathy with the injured one, in fact it was difficult to know who was the one with the embedded bullet.

Eventually they arrived in MIU.

Big Sal started to take down the victim's details.

I was curious. I watched.

"They were cleaning it," Alice said.

"And it went off," Tweedledee said.

"Who was holding it?" Sal asked.

"Don't know, it just went off," Alice said, "and we was watching the telly," she added and all the time Alice talked she played with her red mobile punching the keys and then looking at the thing.

All of a sudden Tweedledee hack-coughed and turned as if looking for somewhere to spit.

Tweedledum scratched the back of his neck, "We was cleaning it," he said.

"The bullet never came out," Alice said, still texting.

"It's stuck in me thigh," Tweedledum said.

"I thought that it would fucking well go right through 'is leg," Tweedledee said.

"His birthday tomorrow," Alice said, "he'll be 30."

"He was lucky it didn't go six inches up," Tweedledee said.

"Would have been his cods," I said.

"What's cods?" Alice asked.

"Me bollocks," Tweedledum said.

Tweedledum was not as thick as I thought he was.

"I'll want the doctor to look at him," Sal said.

"Get his details, I'll phone them through, you want him now?" I asked.

Sal nodded.

I went through my room and into the doctor's room. He was on the net looking at his emails. The screen was covered in Arab script. I cannot figure out how it is possible to read Arab script with an English keyboard. But the Saracen is able to read and send emails with ease.

"Big Sal's got a gunshot wound in MIU," I said.

The Saracen turned, looked at me, "Good," he said, "Just like Baghdad, like being home."

He rubbed his hands. He spun round on his chair. He walked out of the room. He walked down the corridor. He pushed the pump on the liquid cream can.

Clean hands. He walked into MIU.

I pushed the pump, we both had clean hands.

I followed.

"So," he said.

And then he took the large scissors and he cut the victim's trousers and there was a perfect hole where the bullet had entered the leg. It was just a hole and you wanted it to be shaped like one of those transfers that were at one time fashionable things to stick on your windscreen giving the impression that a bullet had passed through and into the car. But it was not like that. It was just a hole, which was full of solid almost black blood, which was weeping a little.

"So," the Saracen asked, "what do you want a silencer on a handgun for?"

Tweedledum and Tweedledee looked at Alice who was already looking at the Saracen doctor.

"They was cleaning it," Alice said.

"Why would two people want to clean a gun together?" the Saracen asked.

"We never thought there was a bullet in it," Tweedledum replied.

"It just went off," Tweedledee said.

"By itself," the Saracen said.

"Like I said, it just sort of went off," Tweedledee said.

"Six inches from his leg," the Saracen said.

"It was further away than that," Tweedledee said.

"It was no further than six inches from his leg," the Saracen said, "and I will tell you why it was six inches away from his leg because there was a silencer on it and I know what happens when a gun fitted with a silencer goes off."

There was silence.

We all looked at the Saracen because everybody sensed that he was about to tell us something important.

The Saracen raised his hand, making a point with his forefinger.

"In my country when we want to execute a man the gun is fitted with a silencer and held not more than six inches from the back of the head. Doing it that way the bullet will lodge in the skull of the victim. It will not blow his face away. It is not good practice to blow the face away. According to our religion it is very bad for the relatives to have to bury their loved one without an intact face."

The Saracen then made the nose tap gesture whilst at the same time he winked, implying that what he had said was passed on confidentiality.

"Do you have a car?" he asked.

Tweedledum and Tweedledee nodded in unison.

"You will take him to Shrewsbury," the Saracen said, "I will write a covering letter for you.

He paused.

"I could take it out here but they will have more time and they will do a better job. Or you could leave it there. In the bone. It will not even move around like shrapnel does. It is well and truly embedded. Of course every time you go through airport security the alarm will go off."

"It throbs," Tweedledum said.

"Lead poisoning," the Saracen said.

"How long does it take?" Tweedledum asked.

" What do you mean?" the Saracen asked.

"To take it out," Tweedledum said, looking at his wound.

And then Alice placed the phone about six inches away from the wound and took a photo of it and then Alice continued texting.

"Depends how it went in," the Saracen answered.

"How long before he dies?" Alice asked.

"What do you mean?" the Saracen asked.

"Before he gets lead poisoning," Alice said.

"He won't," the Saracen said.

And the amazing thing was that Alice never once stopped playing with her mobile phone. She sent out text after text after text and even more amazing was that there was somebody out there sending them back right through a looking glass!

When it was all over, when they had gone the Saracen looked at me.

"I'm going to email Baghdad," he said.

"To tell them about the bullet wound," I said.

"No, that won't impress them but the ambulance will," he said.

10   November

"DENNIS!" a woman's voice called.

It was the 19th of November, just past 5.30 in the evening.

Six dressed capons hanging on butcher's hooks moved as a man's flat-capped head brushed their dead heads.

He'd just thrown a log onto the open range as his mother called.

"Dennis."

"Dennis," she called again.

And she never called him Dennis, it was always Den and the sparks sailed up the chimney as the man turned to find out what his mother wanted and the dead heads of the birds knocked his cap off because he had not ducked after she had called him Dennis.

"Bring the big chair over, yer Dad's chair," she said.

And no one had ever sat in the big chair since his father had died and Dennis remembered when that was.

Last November it was

a year ago

the month of death

that's what his father called

November.

And the son picked his cap up off the stone floor and looked at his mother as the sparks went up the chimney and it registered in his mind that something was not quite right.

"The armchair," his mother said, pointing.

And her son froze because all he could do was to remember November, the month of death because that's when the huntin' starts, that's when the shootin' starts, dull damp miserable shitty November, pig killin' time, the month of death and that is the truth because that's when beasts have to die, when there's nothing for it, when pigs become gripped by horror on the killing bench, the screams echoing till their life just dimly flickers out like a dry wick in a hurricane lamp.

November.

And Dennis had never thought about human death until his father's time had come.

"Bring the chair," the woman shouted at her son in an almost cracked voice.

And her 56-year-old boy with his hat all skew-whiff on his head lifted his father's chair and placed it next to his mother and he lifted the cushion a little as she changed chairs so as to make his mother comfortable and she gripped the arms of the chair as she lowered herself and she said,

"Good, I'm going ta join yer father and I don't want to fall on the floor."

And the mother placed her hands on the table next to a dead fowl; a great capon waiting to be plucked and gutted and she gave her boy his final instructions.

"Finish off the rest because the French mon 'ill want them in the morning and make sure he pays cash 'cause he's foreign and you can never trust 'em and this is as good a time as any, so I'm goin' ta join yer father, I've had enough.

"Sit down Dennis,

by the way

the key to the tin box

is under

the big brass candlestick

on the mantlepiece in our bedroom."

And then Dennis watched his mother die.

He saw her lips open and he witnessed his mother's spirit moving out of her frame and he wanted to do something but there was nothing he could do and so he threw another log

114

on the fire and there were more sparks than there should have been and they spun like a Catherine wheel right up the chimney.

The first part of the old woman's soul left the house at a quarter to six.

It took 15 minutes to pluck the next bird and Dennis ripped the flesh, he pulled the quills at the wrong angle, which was the wrong thing to do.

The Frenchman would not like it but fuck him.

Dennis wished that he'd not thought that word because there was nothing wrong with the Frenchman.

The inside came out easy enough, all the entrails in one long piece.

The Frenchman was strange, he always trussed his fowl. It was so that the bird would keep its shape. The Frenchman would push the legs toward the breast and tuck them tight on the side of the bird.

"It pushes the breast up together, makes it plump like a woman's, bra it uplifts them."

That's what the Frenchman said one day when Dennis had delivered some pigs' trotters and stood watching in the kitchen of the Old Bell whilst drinking a white coffee and eating a *tarte aux pommes*, apple tart it was, but it melted in the mouth.

The Frenchman always used a needle and a long piece of string and he used it to make a knot at the eye and then he lifted the drumstick and inserted the needle into the soft spot in the lower part of the backbone so that the string was anchored into the bone. He was smart because when one of his birds came out of the oven all you focused on was the breast.

As Dennis picked up the heart and the liver and threw them into the white enamelled bucket containing viscera from the other birds, he thought about the barmaid at the Bell and how she used to lean forward so you could see her uplifted parts and when she'd come back from Spain how brown they was

and how that young bastard who worked for the contractor
with his 4x4 must have had his hands and other things round
'em and the bucket was half full and Dennis saw the dark
brown of the liver adorned with the emerald gall and he
looked at his mother who was sitting in the chair

jead

completely jead

stone cold jead

but he had to finish

dressing the birds

The flagstone floor was covered in feathers.

Dennis would suck 'em up with 'Henry' and then he'd
open him up and empty the contents over the fire and there
would be a smell of burning and those not incinerated
would blow all around the orchard ... Jesus Christ almighty
there was still apples to pick, good God above his mother
would not be able to see that cider maker who had moved
into the old mill, the one who'd been on television, who
made different varieties from different species with smart
labels but there was only four kinds of apples in Mrs Evans'
orchard, earlies, lates, cookers and keepers which meant the
cider maker might not want them ... but he 'ad um last year
because his mother arranged it, she did everything.

And now her was jead ...

Bugger.

It was all Dennis's now, there was nothing left but Dennis
and the dog, he could let the dog in, he could give the dog
a name, the dog would no longer be called dog, he'd give
her a name and the cat would not like it, where was the cat?
Halfway through pulling out the guts of the third capon
and Dennis was thinking about the cat and the pigs and the
butcher and now he would have to make the arrangements
for the slaughter because his mother always did that part, he
just took them there in the trailer, drew a net over them and
Dougie would look at them and say immediately how much
they weighed and he was always right and now he would

have to use the phone and ask Dougie when he could bring them and she would no longer shout as he drove out of the gate:

"GOOD BYE PIGGIE-WIGGIES
DEN, DON'T FORGET TO BRING BACK SOME SAUSAGES ON ACCOUNT."

Because she was jead!

Halfway through pulling out the guts of the third capon Dennis thought about the roof, the corrugated sheet iron roof painted with black tar that echoed through the house when it rained, which was why he'd taken to sleeping in the chair.

With his hand right up the arse of the capon, feeling the still warm offal Dennis imagined his mother's innards and her windpipe composed of blue and red rings like the suction hose on a vacuum cleaner ...

With two fingers of his left hand Dennis lifted the bird's aperture wide and pulled out a fistful of entrails all the time thinking about medieval times and a victim being hung drawn and quartered ...

It was the first time he'd felt like vomiting.

He would have to get the Sin Eater.

But he couldn't remember the name of the Sin Eater.

He tried to remember what happened before his father was taken away.

To the church for the service.

There were three knocks on the door. Just like the mon who bangs the door in the House of Commons. Three knocks. And then the Sin Eater entered the house with his face smeared on one side with soot and the other with white ash.

Just like a mask.

Just like a play.

The Middle Ages.

And all them from the Black Mountains was there.

They would have to come.

Their names would be in one of the books in the dresser drawer.

All the uncles, aunts and cousins with their black Welsh faces and frowns, poking around. Trying to figure out how much everything was worth.

The twin branches of the family.

The English side.

The Welsh side.

"If we confess our sins

faithful and just

forgive our sins and purify us from all unrighteousness and lust."

That was what he said, and he leant over the coffin and he put his lips at his father's chest and he sucked the sins out of him, he made a hissing sound so that a soft hiss filled the room and all the sins were sucked up into the Sin Eater's mouth and he swallowed a glass of water and a pinch of salt and he went outside and he vomited up the sins of his father right under the branches of the elder tree. The tree that was never cut.

There would be no Sin Eater because his mother had not left any instructions concerning it.

And anyway Dennis could not think of or remember any sins that his mother had committed.

He shook his head.

And her had left no instructions.

One way or t'other.

Which meant that he would have to make a decision.

Fucking hell.

He'd have to get his mother removed, but she wouldn't go until he'd finished and delivered the birds to the Frenchman, no he didn't have to deliver them, just finish them so that they were ready.

The Frenchman was such a good cook that the car park of the Bell was always full of expensive German and Japanese cars like the great four-wheel drive Porsche, which went off the road because the potato harvester had left a trail of mud after it had rained.

The old Land Rover with Dog in the back would never have gone off the road.

The Frenchman made the best apple tarts in the world and called them *Tarte aux Pommes*.

So that was where the key was, but he already knew where it was, it was just that his mother had told him, which in effect gave him everything she'd got.

Dennis knew what was in the box, the deeds were in the box and the deeds went back a thousand years to that time before the Normans came when the house fell into the hands of the daughter of Ethelred who became the second man.

Only the Evans's knew about Ethelred, Dennis's father didn't want it broadcast which meant that he'd have to tell someone because he was the only one who now knew ... he'd tell Dr Ross when he came, he'd tell him that this was the oldest farmhouse in Shropshire, it was in the charter of 968 A.D. and one of 40 wills left from Anglo Saxon times to the second man because the Saxons called the one who inherited, if it was a woman, the second man but his mother had been the first man ... and Dennis grunted as he pulled the last viscera out of the last bird's arse.

One thousand years of history, a flagstone floor, a tin roof, a bog down the garden next to the midden with three holes, one for himself, which was smaller than the one for his mother which was not quite as big as the one for his dead dad, who had made the hole in the first place when he'd modernised the house.

Before that every one used the cow stalls ...

"Bollocks 'ers jead," Dennis said, and he looked at his mother and he thought about it and he realised that it was perfectly correct and in the right order that she should be dead before him. There was only one problem and that was that she could'na stay on the chair because her'd never fit in the coffin if he left her there.

Dennis walked out to the shed and found two old hessian sacks. He spread them on the floor and lifted his mother out of the chair and laid her out on the sacks. Her legs remained bent. He pushed her knee. It cracked.

"Bollocks and fuck it all," Dennis said out loud and noticed that Dog had walked in and was sitting behind the open door.

"I'll call thee Jess," he said and Jess wagged her tail.

"Bollocks," he whispered, realising that he had given the dog a name and he walked over towards the stone sink and he ran the cold tap because his hands were still sticky with blood and guts and he'd have to phone Dr Ross because Dr Ross was the family doctor and only he could arrange things the right way because he was Dr Ross, the family doctor who had taken over from Dr Hodgson who was the first doctor.

It took a long time for Dennis to dry his hands, not because the towel was damp but because he never used the phone, the only one that used the phone was his mother and she was jead.

He would have to learn to use the phone.

He could use the phone if he knew the numbers.

All you had to do was to dial the numbers.

In the correct order.

Before Dennis opened the door to the old Land Rover, Jess was in the back.

As the Land Rover moved up the A49 one headlight on dip the other on main at just under 30 miles per hour, cars passing saw a border collie moving backwards and forwards behind the tail gate.

Dennis Evans did not know where Dr Ross lived but he knew where the hospital was and they'd know.

He was out to find him!

11 They Yawned Contrapuntal

AT THE END OF THE CORRIDOR in the reception area I saw three nurses. Sitting in a chair near them by the door was a security officer. He wore an expression of complete boredom and a yellow jacket. For it is now the age of the yellow jacket and like the stupidity of weeds in an unloved garden they reign supreme.

There was an atmosphere of expectation. The nurses were waiting for something to explode in an exciting frenzy. They had been there for four hours already and they were chattering to each other in dull monotone mumbles for there was a STABB, (suit tie and briefcase bureaucrat). The STABB was standing at the edge of the gathering. The STABB was also in a state of anticipation.

I was witnessing the setting up of a distribution point for the antivirals that will save the population of our great country from a pandemic.

And the more I thought about it the more I began to question the sanity of a system that needs three nurses, one security officer and a STABB to hand out a packet of drugs with questionable abilities. The prescribing of which was done via a telephone call centre manned by handlers without any medical training whatever.

"Hello can I help you?"

"I have a headache."

"Do you have a temperature?"

"What?"

"Are you hot?"

"Yes."

"Any aches or pains?"

"All over."

"You need antivirals. I will give you a reference number and the address of the nearest distribution point, do you have a pen and paper?"

"Yes."

And the master of bureaucratic card tricks was in position knowing full well that the majority of the population will take the great con hook line and sinker.

The Plague arrived in London in 1348.

It took 10 years for fleas carrying the disease to arrive in Ludlow.

They made the 150 mile journey on the backs of rats.

At the bottom of Corve Street where the river Corve bends there is a spring in the middle of a field.

It is called The Boiling Well.

It is particularly active after heavy rain in the Brown Clee Hills. The fields are on beds of sand and gravel. As the extra water from the river moves downstream it filters up and through the layers of stratified sediment laid down at the end of the last ice age. When it erupts it gives the impression that it is boiling.

It is such good clean water that Gary uses it to make one of his beers.

The Boiling Well.

At about 6.30 on the am you will sometimes see Gary moving slowly along the narrow Linney past the cemetery in one of his vans. He will have been to the secret standpipe collecting water from the well. There will be two 50-gallon barrels in the van, enough for a brew.

The Boiling Well.

It is a perfect ale, it has such a pleasant taste that it makes you want to drink more. It also stimulates the secretion of digestive enzymes and it does have cleansing properties, it will when needed cause bowel movement.

Back in 1358 the population of Ludlow thought that the money circulating in the town transmitted the plague and so all the coinage was collected in wheelbarrows, taken to the Boiling Well and washed.

There must have been something in it because 600 years later NHS hygiene experts have decreed that two dispensers containing cleaning solutions of a chemical nature will be nailed at the appropriate height outside every door leading into any consultation room or ward. Individuals who pass through the doors are encouraged and required to squeeze a lever on each container thus causing it to ejaculate into the palm of the person's hand.

Not only that, next to the dispensers, laminated diagrams that look like comic strips instruct those who cannot read or are dyslexic how to rub their hands together.

In 1358 a victim of the plague would start vomiting, run a high fever accompanied by delirium. The victim would also suffer from swollen glands. Eventually the glands would swell up and suppurate until they split open like an over-ripe fruit revealing a mixture of blood and pus. The victims would lie down and stretch out their limbs as far as possible. They would then bleed from every orifice as dark patches appeared on their legs and stomachs. Sometimes a gland would stop suppurating and then swell again until it once again disgorged more blood and pus.

The only thing a doctor could do was to lance the boil, making two criss-cross strokes.

There were no antibiotics. No painkillers.

The sick died in pain and in a stench of corruption.

In hospitals convicts removed the dead from beds with hooks. Cartloads of bodies rumbled through London's ghoul-haunted darkness.

It was called The Black Death.

Fleas feeding on infected rats carried it.

In the middle of 2009 false prophets spread fear amongst the population of the land.

They prophesied the arrival of a Pandemic.

Humans returning from Mexico in great aeroplanes carried it.

The victims suffered from sore throats. They also had headaches with high temperatures. Some had a runny nose. Once at home they sat watching reality shows on giant plasma screen televisions as if in the shadow of their own destiny. They did not fight against it. They phoned NHS helplines on mobile phones, made a note of a number and sent unaffected friends to collect antiviral drugs from distribution centres. They were also told to wash their hands.

Dark coughs and sighs accompanied the tossings and turnings of the victims.

It was terrible.

They stayed in bed for a week watching more crap television until they were completely brain dead before returning to a normal existence.

The belief that dirty hands transmit illness from human to human still exists after 600 years.

And then as I called into my imagination Pudding Lane and the great fire that solved the problem, there was shouting and a knocking at the south entrance.

Nay, there was a pounding on the door.

After 2200 hours our hospital is closed.

The MIU is locked.

There is no nurse.

There is a bell underneath an electronic loudspeaker, which an individual should push if in urgent need. There is a sign printed in large letters telling anyone how to press the button and talk into the loudspeaker. There is a light operated by a movement sensitive switch that illuminates the threshold and all the signs.

Although our hospital is not open 24/7 there is a duty of care to administer some kind of service to the public. Whoever was knocking and banging a way at the door was demanding urgent treatment.

The bell rang. One of them could read.

I lifted the intercom.

"What is the problem?"

"He's cut himself."

"Where?"

"He's shoved his hand through a shop window 'cause he's rat-arsed."

And another female voice shouted at the same time and in unison that he was also right off his fuckin' 'ead.

Once or even twice a week a male drone will out of frustration shove his hand right through a plate glass window. There is no reason for it other than diet. Since birth fizzy drinks and crisps have been fed into the beaks of infants born into a class of half-wits before they are weaned. Not only that even if they suckle the real tit, the mother's milk will be contaminated with chemicals of an uplifting nature. This is the result of allowing persons without any beliefs or even an inkling of common sense who are unable to support themselves the right to breed.

At the very beginning of the 21st Century society is going down the plughole faster than the Roman Empire did when rich and wealthy Roman citizens used to eat like pigs and then shove their fingers down their throats in order to vomit the food back up so that they could start again.

The Romans invented anorexia and bulimia.

They even invented brothels, which were more civilised than 20/30 holidays young Anglo-Saxon women save up for in order to have as many partners as Claudius's wife Messalina had when she took part in a competition with a prostitute whilst the Emperor was away conquering England 2000 years ago.

We are breeding a dangerous subspecies of humans, who have their own social workers following their every move until at the end of the day someone is at hand to even wipe their arseholes. The under achievers are just like WAGS and Celebrities who have personal trainers, shoppers, bodyguards and other lifestyle trick artists following them around like guide dogs.

The knocking continued. My doctor came into the room. Now Dr Bertrand Bromley served in the first Gulf War. He has therefore seen more blood and guts than Dougie Griffiths sees on a Monday morning at his abattoir in Leintwardine.

"What is happening?" he asked.

"There is a knocking at the side entry," I replied.

"Do we know what the problem is?" he asked.

"One of them has tried to remove a shop window with his fist," I replied.

Dr Bromley started to rub his hands in anticipation.

"Can we open the MIU?" he asked," have we got the keys?"

I answered in the affirmative.

I went to the side entrance. I opened the door. Smells blew in: perfume, tobacco and blood. I eye-balled the monster.

The man who had pushed his hand through a plate glass window was covered in it. Blood was dripping from his trouser leg. He was standing in a pool of blood.

"Wait," I shouted. I did not want blood all over the floor.

It was the fashion years ago to carpet the floors of hospitals. It made them silent. It was a stupid idea. A carpet is very difficult to clean.

"Wait there," I pointed to where he should wait.

"He's bleeding to death," one of the girls shouted.

"I am going to get something to staunch the blood, stop it going on the floor," I said.

Dr Bromley came out to the back door with me. I had opened a dressing. I had a handful of paper towels. The man's shirt was short-sleeved. His arm looked as if it had been sliced with a Stanley knife. The wound was pulsating. His knuckles were bruised. His index finger was bent backwards. Dr Bromley pressed the open dressing right on to the wound.

We all walked into the MIU room. The young women wore heels. When they walked into the MIU suite the heels scraped. The second girl was either sending or receiving a text message. The mobile phone in this country is used in exactly the same way as old men drinking coffee in cafés all over the Middle East use worry beads.

The telephone started to ring in my room.

I looked at the Doc.

He nodded.

We had arrived at the difficult part.

We had a call.

The dispatchers in our control room did not know that we had a patient in MIU.

"Hello."

What they wanted was for us to go to a patient who had been sitting on the lavatory for four hours on account of the fact that he could not get off the pan. His wife thinks that he has had a stroke.

The dispatchers are not interested in the situation in our hospital because they have targets that must be achieved. It is an urgent call and so we have one hour in which to do it. As far as they are concerned the patient my doctor is about to sew together does not exist. I know that it is going to take at least half an hour to even get the patient cleaned and patched up. And I also know that no one else has any chance of reaching the man on the pan, which we would be able to do if a half-wit had not decided to remove a plate glass window with his bare hands. What is more if he had told someone what he had intended to do by way of entertainment that evening then we could have prepared in advance all the gear required in order to prevent the idiot from bleeding to death.

"Hold on for a moment," I said.

"No, better still I will ring you back," I said.

I had to get the details of the patient my doctor was going to sew together.

The doctor was moving him into the room with the black bed and the overhead spotlight.

I walked in. I opened the door to the white cupboard. The suturing gear was all there.

Dr Bromley was in his element. He's also in the Territorial Army. Helicopter blades.

WOMP, WOMP, WOMP.

The Gulf War, Afghanistan. *Apocalypse Now – The Ride of the Valkyries*.

Dr Bromley is a perfect country doctor. The doctor to have around when something happens in a farmyard or a sawmill or when a tractor turns over.

The patient had no idea who he was. Where he lived or what he was doing in a hospital having his arm sewed up. He was completely rat-arsed.

I had to get his details.

The girl with the mobile phone would know.

I sat her down in the waiting room well away from it all. I asked her what his name was. I looked at her cleavage. I looked at the jug handles around her waist. I wrote Wayne's name down. I wrote his surname down. I saw her bad teeth. I wrote Wayne's postcode down. I smelled her shampoo. She did not know Wayne's date of birth. She did not know who his doctor was.

I let both girls outside in order to blow smoke rings and text.

The postcode found Wayne and his date of birth and his doctor. Wayne was a regular user. He was in the system.

I went into the MIU room. I pulled rubber gloves on. Dr Bromley had started to clean the wound. I passed him the gear.

It reminded me of installing a stainless steel chimney in a difficult flue with old bricklayer called Percy who would shout "Forceps," just before I handed him his hammer or chisel.

My doctor started to sew. It was like darning a sock.

It was the same technique as the French chef uses when he pulls together the flesh after he has stuffed a veal breast, and then sews together the opening with fine kitchen string before he secures it with a double knot.

"I'll glue the two small wounds," Dr Bromley said.

I found the glue in the fridge.

I handed the glue. I waited. Wayne came round. Wayne walked out.

Two pairs of heels scraped across the car park.

I got the mop. I placed the debris in the yellow sack. I cleaned the black plastic bed. I mopped the floor. I loaded the gear into the car. I locked the door.

As we were leaving a great 4x4 arrived. We were buckled in our seats. I was about to reverse. A man with the biggest beer gut I have ever seen in my life managed to get out of the driver's seat. He wobbled over to the entrance like a giant Humpty Dumpty. He'd got duck's disease, short legs. The light sensor could not miss him. He could read because he pressed the correct bell.

I looked at my doctor. He looked at me. I unbuckled.

Humpty Dumpty saw me get out of the car.

"Tamiflu," he said, "I've come for Tamiflu, and the call centre sent me."

"It's only open between 5 and 9," I said.

"You the doctor?"

"No, driver."

"They sent me here, you can die from it."

"There is none left, they have given it out. Tomorrow, come back tomorrow."

"But they told me to come, all I want is some fuckin' Tamiflu."

"When did you phone?"

"Eight."

"Yea, but it's almost ten."

"But this is a hospital, it's open 24/7 in'it?"

And then he pulled out of his pocket an iPhone and the screen illuminated itself and he started to dial and the back windows in his 4x4 were all blacked out so that his chariot looked like the kind of thing that the President of the United States would ride around in or that Madonna would arrive in with her adopted African children together with half a dozen bodyguards all wired together with earplug phones and they would be bald headed, just like Humpty Dumpty, only they would be half the weight and fit, with the correct length legs and Humpty Dumpty was talking to the individual who had Swine Flu:

"It's fuckin' closed, they ain't got none."

And he shouted at me, "THEY GOT SOME AT SALOP?" and I nodded, not knowing whether or not they had.

And then Humpty Dumpty turned and he took a deep breath and his belly raised itself as if in a shrug and then he walked back to his 4x4 and he slumped behind the seat and holding the steering wheel with one hand he reversed out of the car park still talking into his iPhone and we followed him out and then I saw the 4x4 leave rubber on the tarmac.

A-speeding into the distance.

Humpty Dumpty was going to Salop.

To get Tamiflu.

Once we were on the road I thought about the dislocated finger.

"How did you fix Wayne's finger?"

"I pushed it back while you were phoning."

I drove.

My doctor reclined his seat.

We arrived at the estate.

The first house had two giant plasma screen TVs. The kind of high tech devices that cost almost a grand each and they had all the curtains open so that everyone could see that they had the things. The one in the upstairs bedroom was the windscreen of a rally car. It was racing through a forest on a dirt road. There was dust everywhere. The car bounced. Sometimes the top edge of the steering wheel was visible. Even looking at it for a few seconds 50 yards away made me feel giddy. In front of the downstairs screen on a giant leather sofa a man and a woman were engrossed in the complicated activities of Big Brother.

In my lifetime Todd A-O, Cinemascope and Vistavision have moved into three-bedroomed council houses together with sound systems with bass notes that threaten the very foundations and tiles on the roofs of the dwellings containing them, never mind about the eardrums of the human sat in front of the things. It is an exaggerated form of realism without any form of imagination, hyper-reality, realer then real.

Two doors down was number 33 where a man had been sitting on the bog for almost four hours.

Dr Bromley went in. I phoned Dispatch. I logged the arrival time.

Dr Bromley came out.

He waved at me.

I got out of the car. I went in.

The patient was still on the bog.

His voice rose demanding that God should bear witness to his situation; he was groaning the groans of a man unable to get off his chamber pot. His arms were raised in prayer.

The toilet in the house was the smallest I'd ever seen. There was no room. There was not enough space for two of us to even enter, never mind about lift the man. There was no way we could move the man off the bog. He had to lift himself up and somehow shuffle to the right.

He started to mumble and grumble until he uttered a powerful growl mixed with an explosion of swearwords emitted like machine gun fire. Suddenly it all ended in a storm of sobs mixed with quiet curses.

Dr Bromley squeezed in. He examined him. He wanted to see if he could be moved.

"He's off his legs," he said, "I think its safe to move him," he said.

"Don't think," I said.

I weighed the situation up.

"I think I can move him," I said.

"Don't think," Dr Bromley said.

I decided to remove him. It would be like moving a 2 cwt sack of grain.

It would be a slow lift. Dead weight.

I moved into the bog and stood facing the trapped man. I leaned towards him all the time instructing him to place his arms around my neck and hold his hands together. All I had to do was to straighten up. Unfortunately the wash hand basin behind me was in the way. An idiot had designed the bog. The architect was a fool. No one had taken into account how to remove a body from a bog. I told the man to remove his hands from around my neck. I looked down. His feet were still in his trousers, which were still around his feet. Instinct told me to remove his shoes. I removed his trousers. I removed his underwear. I could not get over how white his thin legs were. They were covered in some kind of dandruff, white flaking skin. All of a sudden his feet had movement. I returned to the position. The man held his hands together. I felt his weight. He was not as heavy as I thought he would be. I had to straighten my back in a very confined situation.

I knew I'd got him when I managed to place my hands under his armpits.

"Keep going," I shouted.

And I turned holding him closer.

We were now dancing.

All we needed was the music.

A waltz, in triple time.

He was upright.

An instrumental form.

He was standing on his own two feet.

An apt vehicle for composers like Chopin or Ravel.

We were moving.

He would not let go. I waltzed him into the kitchen. I lowered him onto a chair. The man cursed his nakedness.

His wife threw a blanket over him. His grey hair was standing on end.

There then came into the room a period of calmness.

I left my doctor with his patient.

I returned to the car.

I saturated my hands in a sterile liquid.

My hands were clean.

But his smell was still attached to me.

It was the smell of a man wilting, fading away.

The man was drying up inside the shell of his house like an old nut.

I sat in the car looking up at the streetlight. It was a white light with a blueish tint. The colour of death or mourning. The lamp was surrounded by a swarm of June bugs, heavy as bullets. They were fascinated by the light. Some had fallen onto the pavement. The fallen were struggling clumsily trying to fold the delicate membranes of their wings back beneath the hard shields on their backs. They were once grubs living three years underground. They had not long changed from larva to beetle.

They had not long to live.

I remembered one hitting me right in the middle of my full-face helmet.

I was riding a BMW R75/5 motorcycle at considerable speed.

The visor shattered.

The bug spread.

It stank.

Waiting time.

Our life is so complex that humans no longer live in simple round huts that provided shelter from the weather and all the other physical hazards of the world. In the 21st century our lifestyle demands that we sit in front of great TV screens in our own tele-space connected to a digital world, the human brain integrated into an electronic man-machine circuit.

We are part of digital data.

Less than five miles as the crow flies there is a hill fort covering an area twice as big as the estate I am in the middle of.

There would probably have been more people living on that hill fort in round stone huts a thousand years before Claudius conquered the Celts than there are today in this settlement in the digital age.

And they are all trapped, unaware of what is happening around them, unaware that a man has been stuck on a bog for four hours. Any help wanted is obtained by phoning for a doctor 40 miles away.

"We'll get back to you as soon as we can."

If you are lucky you will wait for half an hour.

You will then be triaged which means that you will be asked about your situation which is desperate on account of the fact that every one near you in your settlement is trapped digitally and unable get up from their TV screens.

You need help.

The town needs help.

In fact half the town is as helpless as the old man I have just lifted off the bog.

Three thousand years ago the population of a hill fort would have been more aware of each other than they are today in a wired, plumbed-in Welsh border town where everything is written in two politically correct languages, one of which less than 5% of the population can understand. And what's more if the old man I lifted off the bog needs to be admitted to a hospital then he will have to go to Abergavenny because the local hospital is full.

As I ponder the situation the laptop flickers and I see that the screen is digitally creating another call.

A woman has been terrorising an old mining town called Highley. She has been walking from pub to pub naked, demanding that someone make love to her. Her partner is very concerned because she has locked herself in the bedroom listening to Leonard Cohen.

The problem is that she only listens to one song, which

she has been repeating for the last two hours at full blast.

I worry because this is a mental health situation and will take my doctor an age to sort out. There will be all kinds of trick cyclists to call out as well as social workers and probably the Bill. We are halfway through the night and there is no end in sight and I am dying for a black coffee and a ginger biscuit to dunk in it.

"I have just the ticket for you," I said to Dr Bromley as he buckled himself into his seat.

Dr Bromley looked at the Rugged laptop's screen. He went slack-jawed.

"I don't believe it!"

Dr Bromley made big eyes.

"This is one fucked up world," I said.

I drove out of Knighton. The moon was full. I crossed the border into Herefordshire.

The moon was full. It was bright and there were shadows of trees falling across the road.

Moon shadows.

Somewhere on the surface of the moon is an American flag, a Coke bottle and a Swedish Hasselblad camera. One day Google will map it. They will never find the camera.

"I wonder what song she's listening to?" I said as the Honda moved around the Fiddlers Elbow.

"*Dance Me To Your Beauty*," Dr Bromley said.

"No, *Hallelujah*," I said.

"*Lover, Lover, Lover*," Dr Bromley said.

"*Suzanne*," I said.

"I don't think so, *Joan of Arc*," Dr Bromley said.

"There is only one song that it's going to be and that's, *I'm Your Man*," I said.

"The one where he sings, if you want a father for your child, that one?" Dr Bromley said.

"We'll go for that," we both agreed.

We had great difficulty in finding the house. It was called 'Hope' and it had solar panels on its roof. It also had photovoltaic panels. The roof was covered in all kinds of devices. There was a windmill on a tall tower. It was slowly turning. It was a carbon neutral, self-sufficient dwelling with a Toyota dual fuel Prius in the drive. The only trouble was that we could not find the entrance to the drive. We were in the wrong road, on the wrong side of the house. However there was a gate and a small path leading over a landscaped grass hill surrounded by a wild garden of various planted weeds.

Dr Bromley unbuckled his seat belt.

He coughed. "Over the hill," he said.

He opened the rear door, pulled out his leather Gladstone bag.

"Be careful," I said.

I watched him go over the hill between the stays of the windmill mast.

I called Dispatch. I reclined the seat. I lay back.

From where I lay the linear trajectory of my vision pinpointed the whole of the windmill, framing it in the passenger window. It was a silhouette, moving on its mounting. As I observed the device I became conscious of something else. I touched the button on the armrest lowering the window. The wind turning the windmill was creating a beating sound like a miniature helicopter. It was beating the air. I also became aware that the wind was moving through the structure creating another auditory perception. What was happening was that the currents of air were playing the wire stays like a violin bow. As the tension in each stay altered with the movement of the tower so did the sound. It moved up and down an octave. As this displacement and agitation continued a soundscape was being formed.

I listened deeply.

I concentrated to such an extent that I almost missed two shadows appearing over the brow of the hill. Dr Bromley was running as fast as he could. A naked female was chasing him. And she was as naked as nature intended and she was a big woman in more ways than one. Not only that but she was gaining and then I saw her launch herself into the air. For a moment she was flying. If Dr Bromley had not made an additional effort at the correct moment then the creature would have surely brought him down.

He was lucky.

The moon illuminated the whole thing. She slid down the hill on her belly, her arms outstretched like a million-pound-a-week footballer on a wet pitch.

I saw it all.

And Dr Bromley grabbed the door handle.

He threw the bag at me.

He got in. "MOVE MOVE MOVE," he shouted.

I left rubber.

Dr Bromley said that she was nuts. He said that he should have known, that he had broken one of the golden rules, which is never to visit a patient who has no knowledge that a doctor has been called. Be very careful when someone else calls for someone else. He said that her partner had not told her that he had called a doctor. That when he entered the bedroom she was asleep. That when she woke she said rubbing her eyes, "at last you have brought me a man," and that she grabbed at Dr Bromley, trying to pull him into bed and that he just managed to break loose and he ran down the stairs thinking that once she hit the fresh air she would turn back but that it invigorated her to such an extent that he felt her gaining, that he could hear her feet padding and her cursing and shouting and her wanting.

"I tell you what," I said, "she is not bad looking, her's got a fine figure, I just can't understand why her conna find a mon to give her one."

Dr Bromley sneezed, he fished a Kleenex out of the box, he wiped his nose, he rolled his eyes, "dawn," he said.

"The time when men of reason go to bed," I said.

The doctor yawned.

The driver yawned.

They yawned contrapuntal.

12   Strange Masks

IT WAS THE DAY AFTER the day when the man who winds the mechanism in the clock tower clock fell off the ladder.

It took two and a half minutes to make the climb.

Hand over hand, occasionally looking up at the trap door, why was it already open? The clock winder was the only man to ever open the trap door. The clock winder always saw the dancing dust sunbeam coming through the slit window in the tower, it was a spotlight enabling him to see clearly the second hand on his Incabloc 17-jewel Swiss movement watch that loses precisely three and a half minutes every day.

The clock winder's brain was as regular as clockwork.

That morning, although the sky was June blue, there was no ray of light.

That morning the clock winder looked up and saw a corpse swinging from an improvised gallows.

That morning the clock winder looked up and saw hundreds of flies swarming around the face of a man swinging like a giant pendulum.

That morning the sun coming through the bell tower shone right through a swarm of flies making it look like a knot of illuminated dandelion seeds.

Not only that but the sun's rays also spotlighted the dead man's nose transforming it into a pig's snout full of congealed blood.

SHOCK.

The man who wound the clock lost his grip.

The man who wound the clock took two seconds to hit the deck.

The man who wound the clock broke five ribs and punctured his lung.

He was lucky.

The nurse in the nursing home told me all about it.

In great detail.

I escaped.

I sat in the car.

I peeled a Mars bar.

The sky was as blue as it gets.

There was not a smidgen of cloud and I closed my mouth around the Mars bar feeling the sweetness edge into my teeth, and someone's son had committed suicide, and as I ate the Mars bar I tried to imagine what had gone through the son's mind during the last few hours of his life in the open raftered attic holding the mechanism of the clock.

A human mind degenerating into a wild ferment.

A child of God testing a rope hanging over a purlin or crossbeam before finally climbing over the edge in order to personally face his maker.

I licked the remains of the Mars bar off my finger and thumb and waited.

The morning sun moved higher. The Honda's diesel engine ticked over. The air con forced cold currents. The laptop lay on the passenger seat. The printer lay on the rear seat. Tom-tom was in his sucker. The Third Programme played Khachaturian. The warm air outside launched the greenfly.

I waited.

The best way to get the doctor out from a call is to recline the seat, lie back and pretend to sleep.

I reclined into the horizontal position.

The doctor pressed the door handle. I pressed the lever and eased my body back into the upright position.

My doctor has two daughters; one is 18 and teaches

(during her gap year) scuba diving in Australia. I have never seen her daughters but their mother's DNA will have been well read and replicated during their reproduction, which means that neither child will take any shit from the night before.

"The problem is very simple," the doctor said.

"Is it?" I said.

"But the solution is complicated."

"Is it?"

"Yes."

"The patient has been drinking whisky for three weeks."

"Bender."

"Yes, three weeks continually and is vomiting blood, he's here for respite care."

"A 62-year-old alcoholic in an old people's nursing home?" I put the question.

"Who also snorts heroin," the doctor answered.

"Amongst other things," I said.

"Is also gay," the doctor said.

"Don't tell me the rest."

"A self harmer."

"Aids."

"With bowel cancer and Aids."

"No hope."

A long pause.

"And they do not know what to do with him because there is no one qualified to look after him and what is more they are afraid and they want him out but there is nowhere to put him."

"What are you going to do?"

"I do not know."

"Where did he come from?"

"Stoke on Trent."

"Madness."

"Care in the community."

"But not his."

"He has no family, he has nothing, not even anywhere to go when he gets out."

"Oh dear!"

"And he has nose bleeds because his liver is totally burnt out."

"Cirrhosis."

"They do not want him because they are afraid of him. They don't know how to look after him."

And then my doctor placed her left hand under her right elbow and lifted her right hand up to her jaw and she held her face and she sighed into her hand before rubbing her chin.

"I don't know what to do," she said.

Three greenflies settled on the edge of the driver's wiper blade.

"They have to keep him here until Monday. Monday this guy gets sorted. I can't do anything until Monday. Get the team in on Monday. They have to look after him until Monday, that's all there is to it," she said, reaching out towards the volume control on the radio.

"Khachaturian," she said, turning up the sound.

We both listened to the sabre dance.

I looked at the doctor's face in the rear mirror.

She was weighing things in the balance.

When she opened the door, warm air entered the car and seemed to smooth out the orchestral sounds, melting them into a grey din. I watched her move away from the car into the entrance of the care home. She was holding her mobile phone. She walked with purpose. She had the decision in her head. She walked swinging her hips. Just like a woman should walk when she walks away from a man and knows he is watching.

There were two phones in the car as well as the laptop, Tom-Tom, and printer. The car was full of information technology, a swarm of inventions created by the resourcefulness of human genius, none of which would help the man from

142

Staffordshire with Aids who had tried in vain to solve his problems by drinking Scotch for three weeks, nor the man who had solved his problems in the clock tower.

All modern inventions do is to give rise to exaggerated hopes of communication. Man might just as well make a musical box in the shape of a Chinese pagoda, which when wound, would play a rondo whilst turning like a merry-go-round at the May Fair. Driven by clockwork a device of this nature would be of more benefit to mankind than any form of digital technology.

I looked at the distorted shape of the doctor and male nurse behind the glass door.

They were talking. He was shaking his head. That did not matter, he would have to concede.

It reminded me of the hall of mirrors on Folkestone seafront.

As the Honda moved out of town a delicate resin-scented guilt began to descend in spirals onto the streets below the clock tower and as they passed each other the villagers' tongues moved clumsily in dry mouths and the old yew trees around the church stood like silent witnesses, their arms reaching up towards the deep blue sky.

I drove for three quarters of an hour following Tom-Tom's directions until spread out before us was a large overgrown forest. Tall pine trees, broad apple trees covered with silvery rustling leaves grew above thick tangled grass never cut like a green net. At the edge of this vegetation ran a rivulet of black water, a vein of rotting greasy mud, the only evidence that two hundred years ago coal was mined by hand and carried down the steep slopes on women's shoulders.

There was an electric gate open across a tarmac drive. I could see that each side of the drive beyond the gate the grass was perfectly manicured.

I was arriving at a residential caravan site and looking for number 8.

As we moved up the drive gnomes began to appear. They

were standing on the grass verge. Whoever cut the grass would have to move them. Some were pushing wooden wheelbarrows containing geraniums. One was riding a bicycle. Three were fishing from the banks of the coal black stream. Some had even been copulating because mummy gnomes were pushing prams containing bearded baby gnomes.

The caravans were very close together.

So close that if the occupants had a row then it would be in public. So close that every one in this village of vans would know if ever or when ever copulation between consenting adults took place.

If anyone other than gnomes ever took part in the act then a union jack would be hosted and flown from a full size flagpole standing between the old red telephone box and the waste bins.

What we were arriving at was a camp of third age refugees from the urban lands of the Black Country, all with new cars parked outside caravans, which can never be towed.

I drove around the estate the wrong way and saw gardens and trellises holding hanging baskets containing flowers from various zones and climates. There were patios open to the sky overlooking a grim, overgrown orchard covered in a great rash of weeds from wild seeds liberated in a shameless outbreak of lust.

Eventually a woman waved to us and we followed her almost to where we had started.

A circular tour.

I put the handbrake on right outside a caravan clad in rounded wood, which gave a very good impression of an Austrian ski chalet.

Probably the very worst thing a human can suffer from is retention. Retention is that time in the history of the human male when the tap draining his bladder ceases to function.

To put it simply, the body runs a set of cooperative systems each performing a certain task. The kidneys filter the blood and regulate the fluids, removing the unwanted liquid into the bladder. The pipe from the bladder to the tap, which is turned on or off by signals from the brain, passes near the prostate which has a tendency to expand. This expansion can squeeze the pipe and cause retention. In medieval times the doctor sometimes used a straw inserted through the navel in order to relieve the symptoms. Retention is so painful that sometimes suicide was a better form of relief than having a straw inserted into the bladder via the belly button.

Now in the 21st century a catheter is inserted into the eye of the penis, down into the bladder allowing pee to continually drain into a leg bag.

This is a form of torture every man has to look forward to. Once this happens the male is completely knackered, banjaxed or to put it bluntly Fucked, with a capital letter.

I opened the boot and gave the catheter bag containing all the required equipment to my doctor.

It was the noon hour on a Sunday morning and crazy with heat.

It was that very moment when time started to break away from the treadmill of my existence and run shouting down the road out and over Clee Hill like an escaping vagabond.

I entered the Honda. I sat behind the wheel. I turned up the air con. I wanted to lock the door. I wanted to shut out the summer that was growing out of control.

My imagination was doubling and trebling.

The man inside the caravan was my age!

I saw a white butterfly trembling in awkward zigzags outside the windscreen in the burning air.

The air con sent waves through the dashboard vents allowing a white tint of cold oxygen to descend into my lungs.

I sat breathing conditioned air, thinking about my body, the cells, tissues, organs, and the specialization of form and function of each organ. How they all work inside my waterproof skin, floating in a warm plasma sea. All my organs being told what to do by my brain that senses and controls the activity of my whole being. I thought about the very centre of my brain called the mid brain, the nexus, which times the phases of day and night, the seasons, puberty, menopause and death. Which also makes the countdown into jet lag or gives me that strange feeling after working nights.

The man inside the caravan was my age!

And there were greenflies moving up the wiper blade. And each little greenfly has organs inside it just like mine.

Even a brain.

Even a mid brain.

Even a pineal, primal neuroendocrine nexus inside the centre of its mid brain.

And it can tell the difference between night and day.

And the man inside the caravan was my age!

And the man inside the caravan was having a latex tube made in Malaysia pushed up his dick.

And into his bladder.

And I wondered whether or not it would go in easier if his penis was erect because something would happen if he did not close his eyes before he saw the full bosoms of my doctor swinging like bells in a church as she lubricated the very centre of Chakra Number 2 – The Pelvic Chakra, the sacred sensory chakra called Swadhisthana, (one's own abode).

There would be nothing he could do about it once she started to pull the foreskin back in order to locate the eye of the snake and lubricate it.

Because the man inside the caravan was my age.

I heard a tap on the window. I pressed a button. An electric motor lowered the window.

Her skin had been exposed to real and artificial sun. Her cleavage was wrinkled. But she had not yet given up.

"Would you like a cup of tea?" she asked.

She fluttered her eyelids.

I shook my head.

146

"I had one before we left the hospital," I said.

As she walked back and into her Alpine chalet the phone rang. I let it ring because it is a magical device that answers itself. Truly hands free it will also obey your voice. You can shout at it and it will dial any programmed number.

The voice of the dispatcher came out of the car's loudspeakers telling me that we had a call at Knighton Hospital.

As I leant over to retrieve the laptop in order to read the details of the call which had flown through the air at the speed of light, a shadow started to move slowly across the bonnet of the car.

And then I noticed my doctor standing on the steps of the chalet with the man's wife and they were lifting their faces to the sky, pointing to something with upraised hands. And I too looked and a great hot air balloon floated overhead and the gas flame could be seen exploding and as it exploded it lifted the balloon up and the balloon revolved a little as it moved to a more lofty flight.

All of a sudden there were more balloons and one of them resembled a Coke bottle leaning to the left.

Others had names of the companies that had sponsored their flight. Some were shaped like giant birds; others were shaped like clowns' heads with giant smiles.

As the balloons moved across the silent blue sky like a flock of migrating birds, the heavens resembled an old mural full of monsters and fantastic beasts passing and eluding each other in one strange slow silent manoeuvre.

I got out of the car, opened the boot. Found a yellow plastic sack. Held it open. Watched the doctor dispose her purple latex gloves. Looked up at the hot air balloons.

I twisted the bag tight.

"What's next?" the doctor asked as she squirted an alcohol-based cleansing solution into her palms before rubbing her hands together in order to make them perfectly clean.

"Knighton hospital," I replied.

147

"What for?"

"To certify a death."

"36 miles."

"We'll follow the balloons."

"An east wind."

"From Russia."

"With love."

"Why can't a nurse in a hospital certify a death?"

"They have to be trained."

"A special course."

"Probably two days."

"And there is no money allocated for that purpose."

"No."

"If the wind up there is blowing at 30 miles an hour the balloons will pass over Knighton hospital before we get there."

"But you drive faster than that."

"But they go as the crow flies."

"Only if the wind does carry them over Knighton."

"How does the balloonist steer the balloon?"

"Good question."

"A rudder?"

"Oars."

"The thing only goes up or down."

And then as the Honda climbed up the steep hill towards the A4117 the wind grew weary and blew itself out and the sky stood immobile folding itself into blue streaks and all the balloons could do was remain hanging there until the pilots ignited the gas burners in order to lift their devices into a higher stratospheric layer of moving air.

We moved beneath them at a greater speed in our diesel-powered chariot towards the Welsh hills leaving the balloonists to enjoy their rising and falling in the luxurious monotony of their chosen form of motion.

The corner between the side of the hospital's main entrance looks like a concrete shed. On the wall a telephone hangs inside an acoustic box. The instructions telling a prospective user how to operate this device are written in both Welsh and English.

It was not always so. When I was at school Miss Davis, our English teacher, used to tell us that if ever she spoke in her own language then the teacher would hit her across the back of her head. Which was why Miss Davis used to rap our knuckles with a wooden ruler. Which was why by the time we were nine we could all read and write. There were no dyslexics in our school even the dull had a basic knowledge of the three R's before they were ten.

All the events in my life have been arranged within the time of my life, strung along its length like knots on a length of twine. The longer we live the further apart are the knots. Looking at bilingual notices released from my brain events, which have occurred and are in relation to whatever country or culture the bilingual language relates to.

For example, the reason the Kangaroo pub is called 'The Kangaroo' has no relation to the hopping beast that originates from that part of the world where the water goes down the bath plughole in the opposite direction to ours.

Except to the English.

The word Kangaroo in Welsh is *Cae-ka-roo*, meaning Field of Deer, which is what the land where the Kangaroo pub was called before the great grandfather of Cook's tours discovered Australia.

But, since the English only think with their heads facing England it follows that a place called the Cae-ka-roo will be associated with that hopping beast carrying a baby in its belly pocket even if white settlers only named the said beast two hundred years ago. No one will accept that there was a place with a name similar to Kangaroo a thousand years before James Cook sailed a coal-hauling barque from Whitby halfway across the world to Tahiti in order to watch the planet Venus cross the sun. That done he then found the southern continent, the so called *Terra Australis* which philosophers argued must exist in order to balance the landmass of the northern Hemisphere.

What could have happened was that there was a Welsh sailor on the *Endeavour* from Aston-on-Clun, called Ivor Williams, who saw for the first time a herd of strange beasts hopping along across a bone dry horizon near Bonga Walla, pointed at them and shouted "Cae-ka-roo," a field of deer, the name stuck and was later nailed onto the front wall of his local pub in south Shropshire.

As I waited and searched through my inner memories and landscapes I became aware of an ocean of sound entering through the Honda's loudspeakers. One of the great German composers' music was pouring into my private space.

Beethoven's 9th.

The last movement.

And I have no idea why at that time the Choral started to flow like a structural entity but no sooner had I became conscious of my listening than a chainsaw cut right into the very centre of the music. Its sheer intensity muffled all other surrounding noises.

Some bastard was cutting into a tree.

I looked and saw about 400 yards away, half way up a tree, a tree surgeon waving a chainsaw above his head. He wore a yellow helmet and giant earphones. Long ropes hung from the tree so that if he fell then he would just swing. As he cut away branches of the tree more ropes lowered them so that they gently hit the floor. It was a very precisely controlled operation. But there was nothing exciting about it. If you want to cut a tree down then just fell it. Cut it down from the bottom and let it slowly fall over.

It is a wonderful thing to see a tree fall.

I felt like getting out of the car and telling the idiots how to do it correctly,

"CUT IT FROM THE BOTTOM AND THEN YOU CAN TRIM THE BRANCHES OF THE THING WHEN YOU GOT IT ON THE GROUND YOU FUCKING IDIOTS!"

Not only that but the noise of the saw was plunging right into my life like a blasting fanfare of retina-blistering white light and a man was waiting to be confirmed dead in the middle of the hospital and then someone started up a device that was designed to turn the pruned branches into wood chips which eventually cascaded out of a funnel like yellow darts.

It all turned into a grinding drone intensifying by the second, the air becoming thick with burnt petrol, exhaust gases darkening the sky into a leaden blue haze and then the phone rang and answered itself but I could not hear what the dispatcher said so I shouted that she was breaking up.

"Can't you hear the saw?" I shouted.

But somehow the sounds outside became filtered and so the dispatcher thought that I was going crazy.

"I'll call you back," I shouted whilst at the same time searching for the laptop so that I could see the details of the call I thought was being relayed to me and then I saw the doctor coming out of the hospital entrance with Lin who is a nurse who once worked in Ludlow.

She waved. I waved back and all the sounds stopped, just the throbbing of the engine powering the wood chip shredder.

As the Honda moved away from the hospital the sound of the chain saw once more shot through the air like a million splinters.

My doctor was looking at the laptop.

We were going to Stottesdon.

Swine Flu.

"So, have we got the swabs?" the doctor asked.

"We have got swabs, masks, aprons, Tamiflu, 45, 75 and 30 and we have got all the paperwork which is in a white folder on the back seat in the blue crate which consists of 21 sheets of faxed paper as well as about the same amount of emails which are updated every hour on the hour by a team of one thousand bureaucrats in a concrete lead-lined bunker built three storeys underground during the Cold War at a secret location somewhere in the home counties, where the seat of the leader of the NHS is situated, an organization which in fact is the biggest employer in the world other than the Indian state railways, which covers a country 100 times as big as the UK," I replied.

"I do not want to know that," the doctor said, laughing.

"And we got swabs," I said.

We drove along the Teme valley listening to Alfred Brendel playing Mozart's *Piano Concerto No. 9 in E flat major*.

And I made sure that the speedometer needle hovered between 50 and 55.

My doctor does not like it when the road disappears under the front wheels at a high speed.

When we came to Angel Bank we caught up with a crocodile of cars all following a tractor pulling a trailer. We looked across the sky as we climbed up and over the Bonk, searching for the balloons thinking that perhaps they were still hovering. As we moved past the entrance to the Quarry my doctor pointed.

"Look," she said and there they were, almost an illusion, distant things mirrored through miles of quivering air moving over the Malvern Hills floating in air thinned by the heat of flaming June.

The patient had just returned from two weeks in Mexico.

Fifty years ago the citizens of south Shropshire used to go on holiday to Batty's Island, which is an island situated about a mile up river from the Castle where it is too shallow for the boats to float.

There was a beach and we used to gather driftwood in order to build fires because even in the very hottest of those summer days the water was ice cold and you shivered and your nether regions shrunk and your balls turned into walnuts and you looked at the equipment that had disappeared and you rubbed with wet towels in order to awaken masculine and feminine qualities and then to prove that you had reached a certain age you shared a Woodbine cigarette.

The rich went to Brighton or Bournemouth whilst the trade people had more fun in Blackpool.

Some went on five-pound assisted passages to Australia. They never came back.

That was how far away it was and Mexico is about the same distance and the patient has been away for two weeks and he has a very sore throat and a high temperature on both the Fahrenheit and Celsius scales.

And pigs are like humans.

They have the same organs.

And Mexicans like to eat pig and there are a lot of them living very close together in very unhygienic conditions eating all kinds of scraps and waste and even shit and they have developed a mutant kind of flu called Swine Flu.

Pig flu.

And that is where the problem lies.

Pig flu intruders have jumped down a human throat and because the white tourist lives a pampered life his immune system is less finally tuned than the Mexican's, which is why it takes longer for the well fed and pampered army of white cell warriors to fashion weapons at short notice. The hostile intruder liked what it found and what was more the little swine flu germs liked the air conditioning inside an aeroplane. It is an ideal environment for the little fellows to breed.

All morning, in the Honda, I have been inhaling perfect cold pure air. I am part of the most advanced and intelligent species on the planet.

I love air con.

All humans love air con.

Dull unintelligent simple bugs like flu bugs love air con.

The little chap thinks it's his birthday up there in the sky in perfect clean air. He's going to wait in the air filters for the humans to enter the cabin and then he's going to drop down onto clean surfaces and door handles and bog seats, he will wait for the human hand to touch it and then he will wait on the hand until it moves up to the face and he does not discriminate he will enter any mouth no matter what the colour or gender, this little bugger is the epitomisation of political correctness he will enter any mouth and then once he is inside he will copulate and mutate himself into an unknown intruder that the white cell warriors inside all the passengers will not recognise.

The little bastard will dock and become a parasite.

Antibodies will not cooperate and attack, the immune army will have to learn new military tactics.

They will have to be trained.

You got a war.

Like World War Three!

The battle is called the Swine Flu Pandemic and my doctor is walking away from the car wearing a plastic apron, a face mask and is carrying swabs in order to find out if the man, who by the way would have been better off taking his holiday on Batty's Island or Blackpool, really has got the Swine Flu.

If he hasn't got it then the sight of my masked and rubber-gloved doctor will certainly put the fear of Jesus H Christ right up him and his neighbours who just cannot believe what the dickens is happening on an estate next to Saint Mary's Church proudly flaunting its 11th century tympanum.

13   *The Test*

AND SO IT CAME TO PASS that I reached the age of 68 and was deemed to be a danger to others unless I had a driving assessment. This was not ageism. They do not want to get rid of me because I am too old, they just want to be sure that I am not going to crash the horseless carriage, like run into the back end of a voiture that has stopped without any working brake lights.

No.

The plain fact of life today is health and safety. Our society is afraid to take a risk. Insurance companies are afraid of taking a risk.

If you want to take out life insurance you will need to have a medical. If you take out health insurance and then get cancer you will be no longer insured against cancer.

If I went into a betting shop and asked to see the veterinary certificate of a horse before I laid a bet the bookmaker would tell me to fuck off. And rightly so, it's all about taking a risk.

It's exciting. That's why people bet. They take a risk.

Insurance companies do not take risks. They are not exciting people. They employ people called risk assessors who decide what the risk is.

The driving assessor came from Whitchurch. It is a town 50 miles away in a northerly direction as the crow flies. Or two hours down the A49, which is a typical English trunk road created 200 years ago under the Turnpike Act in order to transport goods by a couple of horses or oxen pulling a wooden wagon with wide wheels. The type of medieval vehicle Constable painted at rest under an English elm tree. These roads were made to certain specifications, one of which was that any two wagons could pass each other in any direction with ease. Trunk roads are still the same width as they were 200 years ago but now the wagons are 30-ton trailers pulled by 300-horsepower tractor units consuming fuel at the rate of eight miles to every gallon.

The A49 is not a very safe road to be on, but it can be very exciting.

The assessor had been on it for two hours.

He was overweight by about three stones.

When I shook his hand I discovered that he had soft fat paws.

He had never done any manual work in his life.

He was about 45.

He had about as much energy as my old grandmother who has been dead for 40 years.

He had bad breath. Let me tell you that he had an acute breath problem; air like from a cavern of dead men came out of his mouth.

"What do you do before you get into a car?" he asked.

"Open the door," I said.

"I'm serious," he said.

"It depends on whether I know it or not," I said.

"Why?" he asked.

"Because if I know the car, then I will get in it and drive it, on the other hand if it is new to me then I will walk round it and give it all the safety checks," I said.

"Which are?" he said.

"Tyres, oil, washers, water," I said.

"What are the tyre pressures?" he said.

"36 lbs per square inch," I said.

"What are the features of the car?" he said.

I did not understand what he meant.

"It's a big 4x4," I said.

"What does that mean?" he said.

"That it gives the illusion that it handles better in the wet," I said.

"Will it not go over all kinds of terrain?" he said.

"Not with the kind of tyres it's shod with at the moment," I said.

"What's it for then?" he said.

"Middle class men with small dicks," I said.

I adjusted the rear view mirrors with the built-in electric motor so that he could see that I was doing so, finally setting each window back to where it was in the first place.

He wrote something inside an A4 pad making sure I had not seen what he was writing. It reminded me of school. I had to suppress a sudden urge not to go around to his door, open it, drag him out and then kick seven shades of shit out of him.

It was only the beginning.

"We'll need that on," I said, hitting the air con button, hoping that it would somehow remove the odours emanating from his lung capillaries.

By the time we had arrived at Craven Arms all the time following three trucks, four cars, and a stock wagon, I realised that he had no idea where he was. South Shropshire was not his area. He was afraid to tell me to turn left or right. He would be all right taking learners around Whitchurch.

Turn right at the lights.

Take the next left.

Straight on at the mini roundabout.

Up there he would know all the hazards. Where to take a victim. Down here he was knackered. But we were moving up the A49 towards his territory.

All of a sudden he pulled a master stroke.

"Tell me what the road sign was that we have just passed," he said.

I had no idea what the sign was. I never thought about remembering road signs. I just look at the road ahead, make a mental note of the sign, and then prepare myself for the different circumstances that might arrive in the event of a slippery surface or whatever the warning sign proclaims.

Since we were coming towards the Wistanstow turn I said, "A left turn."

"That's good enough," he said, "but there were others."

"Is this also a test for Alzheimer's?" I asked.

He did not laugh.

He coughed.

There was a smell like an anchovy's arsehole.

It hovered.

The Honda's air conditioning could not handle it.

Because I was driving at a very safe distance from the car in front, which was the last car in the convoy, a white Nova had arrived right up my arse.

I ignored it.

It passed. It slipped into the gap between me and the car in front.

I was now following three trucks, five cars and a stock wagon.

"How can you tell the safe distance from the vehicle in front?" he asked.

"Three vehicle lengths," I replied.

"If you look at an object like a telegraph pole and then as the car in front passes it, if you count two seconds before you arrive at the pole then your distance is correct," he said.

I thought about it and wondered why I had never done it that way and I counted the said two seconds and it was strange that I was the correct distance from the vehicle in front and I wondered why every vehicle in front of me was at least half the distance I was, which was why the white Nova had filled the gap and I thought about the position I was in and reasoned that if I had passed the whole caboodle on the Onibury straight, when I could have, but would have gone well into the 80s to have done so, then I would have been in a far safer environment than I was now.

"What was the sign we have just passed?" he asked.

"A repeater sign indicating that stopping is prohibited," I replied.

"That wasn't the one I was thinking about," he said.

"That was the last one, look there is another one," I said.

"It was the one with the horse on it," he said.

"It's only valid when they train racehorses at 7.30 am," I said.

By now I was concentrating so much on the fucking road signs that I was creeping nearer to the car in front than was safe and I thus braked rather sharper than I should have done.

The anchovy smell became more pronounced.

The air con could not handle it.

I started to gag.

We were moving over the brow of the hill that then descends into Church Stretton. It is that part of the A49 that is covered in all kinds of red boxes and traffic islands created by half-wits in air-conditioned offices who try to communicate with each other by emails or cell phones. People who spend 50% of their lives attending health and safety conferences and then think it's a divine duty to act like a medieval monk and ram their new found dogma down the rest of the population's throat.

I waited in anticipation for questions about the various road decorations. None came.

At the traffic lights a stationary convoy waited. As the stock lorry in the front of our convoy reached the end of the stationary convoy the lights changed. When they changed for the third time I sensed that maybe we would make it. It was not to be. I tried to remember the road signs we had passed just in case Small Brain decided to ask me what they were.

"Have you ever driven a car in America?" he asked instead.

"Only once," I said.

"Florida," he said, "Tampa Florida, that's where I go on holiday."

"55 and stay alive." I said, "and they pass on the inside lane and they drive on the wrong side of the road."

"We do," he said.

A Chrysler, a big silver Chrysler was waiting on the other side of the traffic lights for a left turn signal. When the signal came the thing turned and passed in front of us.

"Florida," I said, "a car like that and a swimming pool in the back yard, what more would you want."

"Air conditioning," he said, "Everything is air conned, humid, got to have good air con."

I said nothing. There was nothing to say. I just wondered how far up the A49 we were going to go because no matter what happened, until turning back we were not halfway through the test and it had already taken three quarters of an hour.

"What was the last sign?" he asked.

I have driven thousands of miles across all the countries of our great European Community. I have never once thought it prudent to remember road signs that have been passed only to register and act on the ones ahead. To read the road ahead. No one can drive looking in the rear view mirror all the time, however if that was what he wanted then he could have it.

"A sign pointing to the Butts," I said.

"Butts," he said, "what's Butts?"

"Where archers practice," I said.

"I never saw that," he said.

"And before that there was a sign indicating that the path on the right was a bridle track leading over Caradoc," I said.

"I mean road signs," he said.

"Well they are road signs," I said.

"They are not in the Highway Code," he said.

"You never said that," I said.

"That's what I meant," he said.

"Oh," I said, "there was a junction sign to Little Stretton and there was a junction sign to The Hope and there was

160

a sign indication a slippery surface if it rained, but the last sign was to the Butts," I said.

Now it was in the hand of the Lord.

I was now much more relaxed, even though two cars passed at once filling the gap between me and the car in front, so that there was now five trucks, seven cars, and a stock wagon in front and then because of the two-second gap a white van pulled out from a farm drive forcing me to slow in order to maintain the safe distance. If I were going to Liverpool Airport I would have to allow four hours instead of two. The assessor had never had to drive for a living. He would never earn a crust in a cab!

When we passed the 30 mph limit sign in Bayston Hill I heard him open his mouth. I almost said, "A 30 limit," but he said, "Take the next turn left."

I understood what he said but there was a very narrow road with a stop sign at the end of it. It was a very sharp turn. It was the very next left turn and so I slowed to take it, indicating my intention.

"NOT THIS ONE, THE NEXT ONE," he shouted.

"It is the next one," I said.

"I know, but I meant the left at the bollards," he said.

"Do you come here often?" I asked.

"What do you mean?" he asked.

"Is this where you normally take people for their lessons?" I asked.

"When I'm in Shrewsbury," he replied.

I was right. At last he knew where he was on the face of the planet.

He said turn left. He said turn right. He said left at the end of the road. He said take the last exit at the mini roundabout. He said take the next turn right.

And so we drove around Bayston Hill, past every school entrance with 20 mph limits, flashing lights, lollipop ladies, playgrounds, over sleeping policemen, roads narrowing into Give Way funnels, in fact every imaginable piece of crazy road adornment mindless brains inside the safety of an air conditioned council office environment could possible imagine and the more I drove the more worried I became because soon they will nail GPS devices onto the roof of every car and then the mindless brains will monitor every movement of every vehicle on the road and it is only the first step because soon with the aid of Google we will become wired into the web 24/7. Think about it, first the electronic calculator made mathematics redundant, and then the computer with its spell check made spelling redundant and then emails made letters redundant and then Tom-Tom made maps redundant and people send texts on mobile phones ending in smiley faces or miserable faces so that eventually even the alphabet will be redundant and we will move back to hieroglyphics, the only trouble being that they will not be written on stone which means that when our civilisation ends nothing will remain, the only evidence of writing will be tablets of stone, which means that if, in a thousand years time after we have run out of fuel and food and eaten each other through starvation, if at that time in the history of the earth an alien from outer space did a little archaeology then the only thing he would find would be Egyptian! Everything from the 21st Century would be null and void. Our shitty little civilisation would leave no record of its existence.

And then at last he said left at the dual carriageway and I recognised the A49, which meant that I would soon be heading due south, on the way home!

As I drove over the large roundabout and headed towards the Stretton Hills I had the urge to open the door and dump the assessor right on the side of the road.

Instead I picked my nose. I drove down the A49. I read the road ahead. Memorised the signs. Kept the required distance from the car in front. I drove down the A49. The assessor looked at his watch. The assessor looked at the road ahead. The assessor said nothing. The assessor checked his watch. I drove as slow as I could.

"I have to be home at five," he said.

I saw a tractor pull out of the Marshbrook turn. He was pulling a low loader trailer. There was a great big bulldozer on the trailer. His warning lights were blazing. It was the most beautiful sight I'd seen all day. I started to hum. There was no way the assessor would be home at five.

When we arrived back at the hospital I parked and the assessor started to tick boxes. I could not figure out how the boxes worked but eventually he told me that I had scored 30 out of 50, which was a pass. I did not thank him for anything. The assessor checked his watch.

"I forgot about the sight test," he said.

We both moved to the car park. It was full.

"What's the number on the red car?" he said.

There was a red Ford at the very far end of the car park. It was not the car he had in mind.

"V269 EAD," I said.

"What number plate are you reading?" he said.

"The red car at the far end of the car park," I said.

"You have better eyesight than I have, I meant that one," he said.

He handed me a duplicate copy of the tick boxes. I watched him walk towards his car. I rolled the piece of paper into a little ball. I binned it. I walked past the red Ford. It was a W reg.

Sometimes you have to take a risk.

14 Wild Edric

ALL I COULD SEE IN THE OFFSIDE MIRROR was the edge of the pavement.

I adjusted it with the remote lever until I had an image of the front façade of the house where my doctor was, all the time marvelling at the technology and wondering how many little electronic motors were involved in the movement of the mirror.

My doctor had been inside with his patient for at least 20 minutes.

I glanced at my watch. I glanced at the mirror.

Half a dozen glances later my doctor's image appeared. He was standing looking up at the bedroom window. He was lifting himself up and down on the balls of his feet. He looked agitated. I decided to get out of the car. My foot touched the pavement. I slammed the door and walked towards my doctor who was still lifting himself up and down.

"What's going on?" I asked.

"Nothing," my doctor replied.

My doctor was using his Irish accent. It was a warning. He only reverts into the Irish language when he is about to lose his temper or when he wants to control it.

"In that case," I said, "we'll get out of here and move in a northerly direction towards the Stretton Hills where a 60-year-old woman is suffering from constipation."

"I have left the feckin folder in her bedroom," my doctor said.

My doctor is called Dr McCarthy. Sean McCarthy. He is from the west coast of Ireland. Once he loses his cool he has no regard whatever for the English language. He is apt to insert into his sentences any old Anglo Saxon word once used to describe copulation or other bodily functions. The word 'feckin' is an Irish modification. Normally McCarthy uses the correct Saxon word, which is the word I would have used to describe the situation unfolding as we both looked up at the woman's bedroom.

"I have the feckin key," he said holding it in his hand in order to show it to me, "she feckin well gave it to me in order that I could shut and lock the door as I went out, which is what I feckin well did but I inadvertently put the Yale lock down and now the key will not turn the lock because I have left the folder on her bed after making sure that she was all right. She is extremely feckin drunk and upset after losing her husband last year who was a marine biologist and was about to publish God only knows what about the state of the warming oceans and the Gulf Stream in particular."

Dr McCarthy kept lifting himself up and down on the balls of his feet as he talked.

"There is something moving behind the door," I said.

"Two dogs," Dr McCarthy said, "she has two dogs."

"Big ones or little ones?"

"Dogs, just medium-sized dogs," he said, looking up at the bedroom window.

"We will have to get in through the back bedroom window, there must be a ladder, or better still there might be a flat-roofed outbuilding I can climb up and onto," I said.

"The feckin dogs might bite," Dr McCarthy said.

"You never said they were vicious," I said.

"She locked them in the other bedroom."

"Ah," I said, "so she must have got out of bed to let them out."

"I do not know how the feckin tings got out," Dr McCarthy said.

I decided to go round the back of the house to see what was there. I had to go down an alleyway. It was dark. There was some kind of vine growing up the drainpipe. I took my torch out of my top pocket. It is a superb torch. A mini Maglite. It is one eighth of the size of my big four battery powered Maglite but it has 10 times more power from just a pair of miniature double A batteries. I shone it up the back of the house. It illuminated a trellis. I debated whether or not it was possible to climb up the trellis. If I was as fit as I was 20 years ago I would have just held onto the drainpipe and used the trellis as footholds.

There were also railings sticking up like spears.

I could stand on them, they looked solid enough but one slip and I would suffer a similar death to King Edward the Second who died in agony by having a red-hot poker thrust through a horn which had been inserted into his anus on the orders of the great Mortimer, who at that time in our history was screwing the said king's wife in our castle.

It was not worth it.

I continued down the alleyway, which in fact separated two gardens each with a path running next to a low fence. I saw that there were clotheslines running above each path and that on one there was a clothes prop. I stepped over the fence and removed the prop. As I returned to my doctor holding the clothes prop like a long spear, I removed a long piece of twine from the trellis.

Dr McCarthy was still looking up at the window where the inebriated lady was sleeping.

"What in the name of the Holy Mother have you got there?" he said.

From the tone of his voice I could tell that he had calmed down a little. The situation had become more acceptable to him. He was not comfortable with it but he had accepted it as a situation that had happened.

I started to tie my miniature torch to the end of the clothes prop. The idea was that I could tap the window with the end of the torch whilst at the same time illuminating the bedroom, causing her to wake.

"I do not think that will be a very good idea," Dr McCarthy said.

"Well I think it's a very good idea," I said.

"There is somebody coming," Dr McCarthy said.

"They have come out of the pub," I said.

"Hide the clothes prop," Dr McCarthy said.

"Why?" I said.

"Because," he said, and the word fell out of the corner of his mouth.

I thought I understood what was on his mind. I laid the pole down and stood with him looking up at the bedroom window. The two men and a woman who had not long left the pub looked at us. I recognised them. We greeted each other. I explained that we were waiting for someone to open the door. The man and the woman were holding hands and anxious to get to bed. The other man had nothing to go home to. He was undecided what to do. I moved in the direction of the car.

He followed.

"Her likes the bottle," he said.

"That's the problem," I said.

"And once her gets enough in her, her starts ranting and raving," he said.

"That's part of the problem," I said.

"And then all of a sudden her falls asleep," he said.

"That's part of the problem," I said.

There was a pause.

And then the phone in the car started to ring.

"I gotta get that," I said getting into the car.

As I talked to Dispatch the man walked away.

Once he had turned the corner, I went back to my doctor who was still looking up at the window.

"Don't bother to tie the torch onto it, it will put the fear of God into her," he said, "Just tap the window."

I lifted the pole up and towards the window.

I gave the window a tap and like a miracle the woman opened the window, looked down at me and started to scream. It was a scream in the highest octave possible. Each part of her scream split into separate notes like the barbs on a length of barbed wire. I looked up and down the street. I waited for windows to open.

I waited for doors to open.

Once this part of my town contained at least a hundred children. Some were from families of eight or nine. Four was the average. Their mothers would have been sleeping with ears half open. A scream on the scale like the one I'd just heard would have woken not only a street but also half the town. In the 21st century the scream had no effect whatever. No windows opened.

At first I put it down to the fact that nobody with children lives anymore in the old town. The only people who live in the actual town are the settlers from the south who use the old town as God's waiting room. Not only that, none of the males are able to get their leg over on account of the blood pressure pills they take in order to prolong the waiting and even if they did most of the women are barren. Of course the secondary double-glazing and the plasma TV screens with surround sound won't help and then the ever increasing deafness caused from eating aspirins like sweets as a protection against heart attacks, because some want to live in the third age forever. But that did not explain it because the very same people are forever complaining about the noise the May Fair makes and have an ongoing petition to remove it from the town. But the drone from the May Fair is nothing compared to a barbed wire scream.

She stopped screaming when she saw the doctor.

He shouted up to her to come down and open the door.

"You have only just tucked me in," she shouted back.

"I know, but I have left my folder on your bed," my doctor shouted.

"That's what it was then," she said, "I wondered what it was sticking into my back, I'll get it."

Her voice was sleep-slurred.

She disappeared.

We waited.

She held it out of the open window.

My doctor caught it.

He was about to throw the keys up to her.

I stopped him by holding his arm.

"The doctor will put the keys through the letterbox," I shouted.

I pointed my torch at the gratings on the cellar door.

"Drop the keys down there and we kick-start another circus," I said.

My doctor nodded. He pushed the keys through the letterbox.

We got in the car.

I hit the 'Parrot' button. The phone dialled Dispatch. I selected first. I let the clutch out. The car moved. Dispatch answered. I told our departure time. My doctor turned to stash his folder. I accelerated through a clot of dancing autumn bugs rising from the river. The aircon pumped cold air. We passed through town. The smokers outside The Bull watched. They sucked. They filled their lungs. They held mobile phones.

We witnessed institutional sadism implemented by the nanny state.

As I drove my doctor played with his mobile phone. His device has a large screen. There is no keyboard. I am not sure how he does it but when he moves his thumb across the screen another page appears. As far as I could see he had a map on the screen and was trying to pinpoint points of interest. He saw me looking at him.

"I am trying to find out where the castle is," he said.

"Which one?" I said.

"Bishop's," he said.

"Gone, pulled down there is only a bit of a hill," I said.

"It's gone," he said.

"Hundreds of years ago," I said.

"The screen, gone, no reception," he said.

He continued looking at the screen whilst at the same time hitting buttons on a keyboard that had appeared on the screen. He was getting quite frustrated. It came to me that the device gave him some form of comfort and that he would be lost without it.

"It is the Long Mynd," I said. "It has strange properties, the magnetic forces go berserk on account of the lead in the old mines."

My doctor looked through the windscreen. Although it was dark the outline of the great hill was visible like a long silhouette.

"We are moving through that part of the county where mobile phones refuse to work," I said, "there is no scientific reason for this. There are masts with parabolic reflectors pointing in various directions but it does not matter where you stand holding the device or where you point it, reception is poor or non existent."

"We have places like this on the west coast," Dr McCarthy said. "It is the Granite," he said.

"Do you believe in fairies?" I asked.

"My grandfather used to leave food out for them," he said, "but my father always shook his head until he started to look after the playing fields and then no matter what he did he always found stones on the field before he cut the grass. No matter how many stones he removed there was always the same amount on the pitch before he mowed the grass and I mean big stones. Grandfather told him to leave out whisky for the little people, just a small glass. He did and then it stopped or at least there was not so many. He used to talk to the little people when he rode on the mower, so that eventually he did believe in them."

"Some believe that there is a porthole on the western side

of the Long Mynd. This porthole sometimes opens giving access to the underworld where Wild Edric and his wife Godda are buried under the lead," I said.

"Why?" Dr McCarthy asked.

"Because he was a bad boy," I said, "he would not submit to Norman rule."

"Good fellow," Dr McCarthy said.

"He was a Saxon thane who married a fairy," I said, "if you believe in such things they exist."

"Fay is another word for fairy," Dr McCarthy said, "It was used in Victorian times to describe anyone who was on the gay side."

"Edric found his fairy, Godda, in the Clun Forest," I said. "She was dancing in a clearing surrounded by six young girls. Forests back then were not like they are today. They were oak. Oak trees need space. Oaks have big branches. Chestnut, walnut, horse chestnut, sycamore, cedar and laburnum, not to mention the wretched Japanese larch did not exist in this land until the likes of Sir Walter Raleigh brought them in.

The forest a thousand years ago was oak.

Deer, pigs and other beasts roamed and browsed in glades and clearings and were hunted by sight hounds which were forerunners of greyhounds and looked like lurchers. That's what Edric was doing. He was hunting and he found a wife."

"It sounds like an Irish legend," Dr McCarthy said.

"Saxon mixed with Celt," I said.

"What happened next?" he asked.

"Well," I said, "Since Edric was a Thane and had all the rights of the Lord of the Manor nothing was going to stop him from having the maiden. Not only that but he had strange feelings in his nether regions and so he made the decision then and there right on the very spur of the moment to snatch the creature. However as he did so, the other six girls changed into wild savage cats as big as hunting dogs and Edric pulled out his sword.

"Don't kill my sisters," the maiden shouted.

Edric sheathed his sword, and turned and saw that the six cats were no longer following. Letting out a sigh of relief he gently kicked the horse with his heels and noticed starlings rising in flocks and making strange patterns in the sky. And then a strange thing started to happen, as the horse galloped six enormous, heavy butterflies flew past and the air shook with a coloured ferment as the creatures decomposed in mid air.

As the remains of the butterflies fell to the ground still fluttering their wings the heavier the girl became, it was as if she was being filled with water that she was being transformed from an ethereal object into an earthly being.

When they arrived at Edric's Manor the fairy walked into the great hall and sat by the fire and her hair started to glow the colour of molten gold.

She sat in the corner next to the fire throughout the night and all the next day and she sat like that for three days and nights all the time watching everything and every movement in the house, like a great cat.

Those three days were extra days, freak days which grew like mushrooms on an old stump and as they reached maturity they fell back into the archives of time so that Edric's people referred to them as chapters inserted in the great book of that year.

Now the cook's house and kitchen adjoined the Great Hall and the cook was a master cook whose name was Richard but went by the name of Cookie and was a very important person who had an apprentice. On the morning of the third day, Prentice made a move towards throwing a log on the fire in the great hall but Cookie stopped him.

Cookie pointed to the golden flames going up the chimney whilst at the same time digging his elbow into Prentice's side.

"There ain't any ash in the grate, Prentice," Cookie said.

On the third morning the girl by the fire spoke: "I know

who you are," she said to Edric and strange octaves of colour started to move as the words came out of her mouth.

And there was a new smell in the air and a different consistency of light and the people of Edric's manor house knew that they had entered a new era.

"You are Edric," she said, "the one they call the Wild, but I have watched you and I have not seen a wild man but I have seen a man who is straight and true and I know that you would marry me and I will marry you but first you must know who I am. My name is Godda and I am Queen of the fairy folk who live under the Long Mynd. It is from my six sisters that you have stolen me, but I will marry you and I will live with you as a human and I will bear you one son and I will bring you luck and wealth, but I will give you a warning and this is it.

If ever you ever reproach me with who I am, where you found me, or mention my sisters whom you stole me from, if ever you do so, I will return to the land beneath the long mountain and you will never see me again.

Now, do you swear?"

Edric swore the oath and the impossible became real.

And then there was the wedding. And what a wedding it was. Four hundred guests bearing gifts and the Welsh princes, Bleddyn and Rhiwallon from the Black Mountains brought Godda a golden torque. Now since Wild Edric lived nearer than ourselves to the cradle of the world he and his friends were endowed with appetites far larger than those of today.

Let me tell you this.

The feast started with the passing of the Pootle. This was the drinking device that looked like a wooden bowl. It was a device turned on a lathe and contained four pints. The inside of the Pootle had eight wooden pegs sticking out. These pegs measured the depth of the liquid, the distance from each peg being half a pint. The Pootle was passed from one to another and the drinker drunk down to the next peg, a half pint being in those days a mouthful or what they considered to be a comfortable amount to swallow.

Eating with their hands the guests detached a wing, swallowed it in two mouthfuls and then cleaned their teeth by eating the neck of the bird before taking a draught of Ale by way of an interlude. Next they attacked the legs and ate them in the same manner as the wing, tossing the bones to the mouths of waiting dogs who fought and growled at one another, all the time the Pootle was passed from hand to hand and woe betide you if you drank below the measure.

That was where the old saying *I'll take you down a peg or two* came from.

Pass the Pootle!

Next came ox ribs briskly eaten down to the ivory.

Now the Anglo-Saxons also ate an abundance of beans and peas and whilst the eaters tossed mouthfuls of food into their mouths they talked, laughed and farted.

Seven months later Godda's belly began to swell and one morning the Long Mynd was shaken by an earthquake force six on the Richter scale and the whole length of the mountain was engulfed by a dense black cloud. Out of this thick vapour a huge black wolfhound appeared. An Earth Mother who was in turn followed by a donkey followed the great dog. There were panniers on the donkey held by a leather straps fitted with gold buckles. A shepherd watching his flock on the Stiperstones said that the Devil's chair held phosphorescent rocks for three nights and glowed like a glow worm's arse.

When the midwife, for that's who the woman was, delivered the child two months later, it was born with its umbilical cord around its neck. It was a very good sign, indicating that the child would be a king or at least a great leader.

The cord was left on the child for seven days. On the seventh day it dropped off indicating that the birth was complete. On the eighth day, the day of speech Gooda was visited and congratulated and the baby was called Alned."

"So how did they all end under the mountain," asked Dr McCarthy.

"If you look at the Tom-Tom," I said, "you will see that we should arrive at the old vicarage where the patient resides in less than three minutes for it is less than one hundred yards and since the thing is correct because I knoweth the way, I shall continue with the legend of Edric the brave Saxon who knew how to pass the Pootle and reigned before the Normans came after you have administrated your healing powers to the fat lady."

The old vicarage in the village of Brampton on the Rock, known as 'The Rock', was built next to the manor house on account of the fact that the Squire who lived in the manor built the vicarage as a form of penitence or ticket for the ride into heaven after belonging to the Hell Fire Club. Since members of the club chased half naked ladies around the grounds of the great manor house riding specially designed hobbyhorses, wearing leather cod pieces, whilst at the same time shouting "Tally-ho" between blowing blasts on hunting horns the vicar's house had to be a first class ticket to the golden gate. It had eleven bedrooms on the first floor alone, as well as a great drawing room, smoking room and library containing eleven hundred volumes of all the great classics.

I looked up at the 28 chimneys and thought about that time when six Bishops stopped in the vicarage for a week back in 1956 in order to exorcise the poltergeist in Sibdon Castle.

I parked outside the front door of the manor. There was a great brass doorknob in the centre of a brass plate. I parked between a great Nissan pick-up truck with an Indian name and a Range Rover.

Dr McCarthy had taken a pocketful of Micro-lax with him. I tried to imagine how he would insert them into the fat lady's rectum.

I hit the Classic FM button.

A female DJ told me that she was about to play *The Ride of the Valkyries* by Herr Wagner.

I turned up the volume.

After 10 minutes Dr McCarthy came out of the house without his bag.

I turned down the volume.

Dr McCarthy opened the door looked at me and said, "Doom and gloom, tis like going into an old antique shop, dark furniture, heavy chests and tables with chairs nobody ever feckin sits in and the walls are hung with old paintings of the open sea or woods complete with stags at bay and sun rays coming through trees, and clouds and nothing going on in any picture, by the way do we have an oral purgative?"

"We have," I replied.

I found a plastic bottle of Glycolax in the side pocket. I handed it to him.

"Fan-bloody-tastic," he said.

He closed the door.

I turned up the volume.

Whilst the fat lady drank half a bottle of Glycolax, the Valkyries rode right over the hill.

A few minutes later Dr McCarthy came out of the door.

He was carrying his bag.

"Let's go," he said.

I reached towards the button on the dash, which would automatically dial Dispatch.

"Let's go NOW," Dr McCarthy ordered.

I took off. The 4x4 Honda grabbed the gravel drive.

"Even the vehicles are obese," Dr McCarthy said.

"I have never seen a pick-up as big as that," I said pointing towards the Nissan.

"Each thigh was as big as me," Dr McCarthy said shaking his head.

"How many Micro-lax did you use?" I asked.

"None, insertion was impossible," he replied.

"Just the bottle of Glycolax," I said.

"Half a bottle, if there is a result then it will be an explosion of enormous proportions," Dr McCarthy said, "and what is more we will be wanting to be as far away from the source of the explosion as possible."

"It is rather like a French goose from that region of France where they produce *pate de foie gras*," I said, "they nail the feet of the bird down on a wooden floor so that it cannot move and then stuff food down its neck by means of a funnel, force-feeding the thing until such time as the liver becomes engorged. I wonder whether or not human organs become enlarged like the French goose?"

"In much the same way," Dr McCarthy replied.

"It's a madness," I said.

"The human's normal state is one of semi hunger," Dr McCarthy said, "and the way to have a healthy life is to continue in that vein, to cultivate a form of tolerable starvation. Diets, exercise and the like are all bollocks. The human was designed to tolerate semi hunger."

"This car needs fuel," I said, driving towards the filling station.

We came out with a full tank.

Dr McCarthy yawned, he stretched and he blinked.

"So how did they all end up under the mountain?" he asked as he removed eyestrain goo from the corner of each eye.

"Who?" I said.

"Our man Edric," he said.

"Ah, I forgot," I said, "I think I must have Alzheimer's coming on."

"Since he had an Elf-maiden for a wife he must have hit her or mentioned her sisters," Dr McCarthy said, "the whole thing resembles an Irish legend."

"Celtic," I said.

"Or a Nordic saga," Dr McCarthy said.

"English folklore is one and the same," I said.

"Tis the oral tradition," Dr McCarthy said.

"It all happened before 1066," I said. "Edric went hunting, he got complacent, he started taking his wife for granted, he went hunting and he got on the ale. He came back pissed, or half pissed and she was not in the house. He looked everywhere for her, he called for her to come; he shouted her name in vain. He went mad so that when she appeared he shouted at her "YOU FAIRY BITCH, YOU HAVE BEEN WITH YOUR SISTERS ... as soon as he mentioned her sisters, she vanished. Edric was left shouting at a cloud of thin air. He went mad. He cried out day and night. He cried out against his own folly. He went manic for seven days and seven nights. On the seventh night the Normans came. It was 1067 one year after the battle of Hastings. It was that time in our history when the Normans decided to extend their land holdings at the expense of the English thanes. The Normans had the writ. They held it for Edric to read. He reached for his sword. The Norman was fast. He held a dagger to Edric's throat. The other Norman held the writ. Edric's son Alned was seven years old. Half a Fay-elf. Each year the boy had grown as fast as an earthling grows in three years.

Three sevens are 21 and he could move as silent as a cat.

He came from behind the Norman who was holding the dagger at his father's throat. Alned was holding a broad axe. He lifted it high above the Norman's head. When he brought it down it was like splitting a log. The axe went right down the very centre of the Norman's spine turning him into two sides of meat. The axe divided his bollocks hitting the stone floor between the Norman's legs where it created a ball of sparks. As the ball rolled Edric drove his sword into the other Norman's stomach. His guts spewed out. It was the start of a private war between Edric and the Normans. It was revenge and not revenge eaten from a cold plate, it was instant.

With the Welsh princes, Bleddyn and Rhiwallon Edric sacked the city of Hereford. He then retreated back into the

Welsh hills coming out of hiding to fight the Normans at York with the thanes Waltheof, Gospatrick and Aetheling. In York Castle Ealtheof slayed 100 Frenchmen with his long broad axe as they tried to escape from the castle. It all ended up in heroic verse written in the Chronicles.

Edric was a man possessed with the will to die. The Normans had to kill Edric three times. The third time the dead souls of Edric and his men rode towards the Long Mynd. It was that time of the night when the false dawn is said to appear. When there are three minutes of light before the sun appears above the horizon. The porthole opened. Edric and his slaughtered men rode into a parallel universe to live for all eternity with his Fairy Queen."

"It is a fine Celtic legend," Dr McCarthy said, "it is a shame the old oral tradition has all but died, that the fairy stories are no longer told."

"Not true," I said, "Star Wars, Harry Potter, Superman or Spiderman or even Groundhog Day, they are all fairy stories."

When we arrived at the Hospital there was a man sitting next to a woman on the bench outside the door. There was a pool of blood beneath the bench. He was sitting with a towel wrapped around his arm. I recognised him. Mitch fits windows. Double glazed windows. A breeze kicked up. Fallen dried leaves swirled.

"Never mix old glass with new," Mitch said.

He was as white as a chalk.

We heard the siren.

"There was nobody here," Mitch said.

"I'm sorry we called the ambulance but there was nobody here," his wife said.

The ambulance arrived. The paramedics got out. I punched the code. I opened the door.

Mitch sat there. He was afraid to move. His wife started to cry.

"It always looks worse than it is," Dr McCarthy said.

"His thumb's almost off," his wife said.

"We'll take a look," Dr McCarthy said.

I opened MIU. They all walked in. I took the doctor's bag. I made tea. Mitch is self-employed. His wife started to sob. Dr McCarthy unwound the towel.

"I'm going to clean the wound," he said.

We all drank tea.

Dr McCarthy finished cleaning. He removed his gloves. I offered tea. Dr McCarthy drank his tea.

"Give yer man some hot sweet tea," Dr McCarthy said, "then I'll sew him up."

The mobile in my pocket rang. The phone in the office rang. I had forgotten to ring Dispatch. The ambulance crew walked out. I lifted the phone. Dispatch was not happy. We had another call. Thirty miles away. Right in the middle of Kilvert country. Clyro. Chest pains. SOB. Son of a bitch. Short of breath. Urgent.

"It's one hour away," I said.

"It's an urgent call," Dispatch said.

"But my doctor's about to suture a patient," I said.

"Not one of ours," Dispatch said.

"He was sitting on the bench outside the door when we got back," I said.

"We have no details, you have to go out to the call, we have to meet the target," Dispatch said.

"We can't go out because the doctor is going to stitch up a patient, like now," I said.

"Tell the doctor he's got to go out to the urgent call first," dispatch said.

I replaced the receiver.

How can you explain to a dispatcher in a call centre 40 miles away that you know the person who needs medical attention? That in a small town where everyone knows everyone sometimes you just cannot send the patient away.

The phone rang. All calls are recorded. I let it ring. I might say something I'd regret.

As I walked down the corridor I looked at the photo of our hospital from the air. My doctor had started to sew. I watched. It was just like my mother darning a sock. I removed my glasses. Rubbed my eyes. The alcohol in the antiseptic handrub made tears.

My doctor sewed.

He tied little knots.

I asked Mitch's wife for her husband's date of birth. I filled the forms. I rang Dispatch. Not happy. The dispatcher scaled her voice up sequentially. She started to rant. In A major. She had no option, she had to take the details.

I opened the door to the MIU. Smells came out. Antiseptic. Mitch was holding his wife's hand. My doctor was making the last stitch. My eyes were running.

I started to clean away the debris

My doctor and I were doing double shifts.

Thirty miles away a patient had chest pains and was SOB.

15   *The Death of the Falcon*

THE CAT SNARED A MOUSE behind the old candle factory. The cat prowled. The cat paraded. The cat saw a man on a mobility scooter drive into the yard.

The man on the scooter skidded on loose gravel before he stopped in front of the up and over door. He wore a gamekeeper's jacket and a flat cap turned back to front. He wore a pair of motorcycle goggles. He put his right hand into his pocket and pulled out a device like a TV clicker and pointed it at the door.

The cat heard the mechanism in the door move and watched the door open.

As the scooter moved over the threshold the man lifted his right hand pointing it behind him and pressed the button that closed the door.

The cat saw it all.

The mouse moved in the cat's mouth.

The cat threw the mouse into the air.

The cat caught the mouse.

One chomp ... *adieu.*

Inside the old factory there were three rows of halogen lights hanging on twin cables.

Twelve in each row, a total of 36 lights.

Six lights illuminated a Formica bar complete with optics and a real ale hand pump.

Three lights were aimed at a 6x4 photograph of Jane Russell. The other lights in the first row were focused on a giant ottoman sofa.

The windows were blocked out and all the walls were clad in acoustic foam as was the rear door.

There was also a sound baffle made from 24 full size egg boxes spray-painted matt black. The baffle stood between a pair of Wharfedale floor standing speakers, which were supplemented by a pair of miniature Mission speakers hanging from the ceiling. On the right hand wall a shelf ran the whole length of the building. It was illuminated by 12 spotlights and was divided into three.

Nine cubes 13 x 13, each one holding about 50 12-inch LPs occupied the first part. Next there was a valve amplifier and a pre amp, which was next to a turntable driven by a white elastic band. At the side of the equipment the shelf was covered in green baize, so that you could prepare the LPs with various cleaning devices prior to playing. The rest of the shelf held another nine cubes. Containing the same amount of LPs.

There were about 1000 LPs in the building which had morphed into a soundproof studio.

The man on the red chariot now inside the studio was called Crutch. He had been given this name after he ran out of road whilst riding a Honda 750 Four in the direction of Switzerland, attempting to reach a gig in the town of Berne. Forty years after he laid the Honda down he still walked with the aid of a walking stick.

He was a piano player who had such a spread to his hands that he could stretch a twelfth flat with either hand and he would throw each hand up in the air when playing in a flashy manner that he had copied from Duke Ellington, whom he saw at Antibes Jazz Festival in 1966 when 'The Duke' accompanied Ella Fitzgerald.

Crutch parked his chariot next to a great Wurlitzer jukebox.

On the other side of the jukebox was another parked chariot.

Crutch lowered himself from his chariot and leant on the side of the Wurlitzer. He paused. He removed the goggles.

He turned his cap the right way round. He listened. All he could hear was the sound of a record trapped in its final groove.

Crutch felt the hairs on his head began to move. He grabbed his aluminium walking stick from the rear rack on his chariot and moved across the room dragging his right foot. He looked over the bar and saw the Falcon sitting on the floor with his feet jammed up against the refrigerator containing a keg of beer. Crutch shouted at the Falcon for him to get up.

"What are you doing down there?" he shouted.

There was no movement from his friend.

There was a soft broom leaning against the bar. Crutch grabbed the broom. He hooked the broom around the Falcon's arm and pulled. The Falcon just collapsed against the refrigerator.

Crutch moved as fast as he could to the other side of the bar. He knelt down on his knees and pulled his friend until he was lying flat on the floor.

His friend was still breathing.

With all his strength he pulled backwards, turning his friend on to his side as he negotiated the corner at the end of the bar.

The Falcon was 6 feet 2 and weighed 16 stone.

Crutch wanted the Falcon on the ottoman.

Crutch sent an electrical message from his brain that he should synchronize all his working nerves and muscles in his arms and legs in order to make the final lift.

Crutch prayed. Crutch struggled. Crutch thanked God. Crutch looked at his friend lying on the ottoman.

"What do you want my good kind Christian friend?" he asked him.

The Falcon looked at Crutch. The Falcon lifted his right hand and pointed towards the turntable. Crutch understood. He moved across the room and lifted the pickup arm out of the repeating final grove of Jeff Beck's *Blow by Blow*.

He went back to his friend.

"Mingus, *Erectus*," the Falcon said.

Crutch understood.

He found it halfway down the shelf. He would have to clean it. He removed it from the sleeve. He pressed the cleaner into the grooves in a circular motion. He placed it on the turntable and lowered the pickup directly into the first groove just as the Falcon would have done.

And the notes from the double bass exploded as the needle in the groove transmitted the vibrations into the pre amp and the valves of the power amp glowed and the whole room started to vibrate as the notes from the speakers fell out and bounced on the pine floor and Crutch knew why the Falcon had such a floor. And the Falcon beckoned Crutch to come to him. And he did so. And the Falcon asked for a drink. And Crutch took him a double Scotch imported by Tanners from Scotland.

And then the Falcon asked for a cigar.

Behind the bar the Falcon kept a pack of green cigars. They were in a leather pouch. Crutch prepared the cigar by cutting off one end with a special clipper designed for the job.

After the cigar was fired up Crutch went outside through the back door and using his mobile called for an ambulance.

When he returned the Falcon beckoned him to come to him. And he did so. And the Falcon gave him his cigar. And his friend lifted his glass to his lips but the Falcon could not swallow, instead his head fell to one side.

Crutch took the drink from his friend's hand and placed it on the floor in order to hold his friend's head.

All of a sudden Mingus's bass went mad and the sounds from the speakers were moving like waves through the air and the air was full of notes turning into exploding black and white butterflies.

Crutch held the Falcon's head until the very last breath.

Crutch had no idea how long he stood looking down at

the Falcon. He only turned away because he heard the lock moving on the garage. He saw it open.

The man who had arrived on the second mobility chariot was a bass guitarist whose name was Byron Jones, better known as Shaky. He was called Shaky because he had a tendency to shake like a dervish once his brain moved into the core of a number.

He wore a deerstalker hat complete with flaps. He had a pipe in his mouth.

It was a large pipe, burning in the correct manner giving the impression that a steam engine was moving under a bridge as he passed through the door.

Shaky drove towards Crutch who had turned towards him.

"He's just dropped dead, the bastard dropped dead on me," Crutch shouted.

Shaky removed his pipe from his mouth and placed it in a holder on the handlebar of his chariot especially created for that purpose. He then drove across the room, stopped in front of the amplifier turned down the volume and drove back to Crutch, where he stopped, turned his seat sideways and slowly slipped out of the saddle.

"When?" he said.

"Just before you came in,"

"Erectus was his favourite piece,"

"I put it on for him, he was behind the bar,"

"Pulling a pint,"

"No he was collapsed, feet on the fridge,"

"Wedged,"

"Not quite, I dragged him around and managed to get onto the sofa."

Since Shaky had not closed the up and over door both men saw another chariot coming towards the open door.

The individual driving it had a long white beard. He wore a red baseball cap, dark glasses and looked like one of the ZZ Top guitarists. In fact the only musical instrument he could play was the gramophone.

It was Walking Joe.

Walking Joe once spent two years living with an aboriginal tribe in the Australian bush. He was as thin as a rake, a Pulitzer Prize winning journalist as well as an alcoholic who swore with great authority on both scales.

"What the motherfucking hell is going on?" he shouted.

"The Falcon's dead," Crutch said.

"When?"

"Now."

"What the fuck from?"

"We don't know."

Walking Joe jumped off his chariot.

Joe was not a cripple. Walking Joe had walked right across Australia and back again. He had also been a fell walker. He was a fit 75-year-old who was able to move in any direction he wanted. It was just that on occasion his legs were liable to collapse, if he miscalculated the consumption of certain beverages.

Walking Joe felt the Falcon's pulse.

"The bastard's really gone to his fucking ancestors," he said.

Walking Joe coughed as he moved across the room shaking his head. He went behind the bar and poured himself half a glass of whisky and then a half pint of beer. He splashed the whisky with beer before he took a slug. He walked back to his friends.

"Might as well finish his cigar," he said.

"Might as well set um up, going to be the last drink here," Crutch said.

Shaky nodded, tapped his pipe on his chariot's handlebars, looked at it, tapped it, and looked again before adding additional tobacco.

Crutch looked at Shaky bending the flame from the gas lighter into the bowl of his pipe.

"It had to end some time," he said.

"But it ended in the wrong order," Shaky said.

"What was that?" Walking Joe said as he relit the Falcon's cigar.

"The wrong fucking order," Shaky shouted.

"What der yer mean?" Crutch asked.

"What I mean is that if one of us other than Bill Faulks, the Falcon, had kicked the bucket first, then the enterprise could and would have continued," Shaky said lifting his drink to his lips.

"Worst thing of is that he was the youngest," Crutch said.

"Sixty eight," Walking Joe said.

"Almost 69," Shaky said.

"You mean that just because I'm 77 that it should have been me, well fuck you pink," Walking Joe said.

"He means that it is paradoxical the Falcon being the youngest," Shaky said.

"Big words gonna fuck your brain up," Crutch said.

"And all this was his idea, his," Walking Joe said, waving his hand.

"We were a quartet," Crutch said.

"And now we are three," Walking Joe said.

"A trio," Shaky said.

There was silence.

Crutch sniffed air and cleared his cranial duct.

Walking Joe looked at the body of the Falcon slumped across the old leather ottoman.

The three men drank and smoked in silence and the only sound left in the room was the sound of a needle trapped in the endless groove of a 40-year-old vinyl LP.

"That was what hit me when I came in," Crutch said.

"What,?" Shaky asked.

"The noise of the needle," Crutch said.

Walking Joe lifted himself from his stool and moved directly towards the turntable, lifted the arm and placed it into its holder. He then moved past the four chariots, toward that part of the garage where they had made a urinal.

It was a perfect solution to the problem of urination.

Walking Joe unzipped and let his urine rip onto the edge of the great tin funnel that was connected to a hosepipe, the end of which finished right in the centre of the Falcon's compost heap. It was an ecological masterpiece.

Walking Joe shook the dewdrops. Walking Joe zipped and paused as he passed the bar and looked at the 6x4 poster of Jane Russell.

"It took Howard Hughes two years to design that bra," he said.

"That's what I call a cleavage, the Falcon used to say," Shaky said.

"The Falcon's dead," Crutch said.

"Is there any money in the till?" asked Shaky.

"Probably," Crutch said.

Crutch moved around to the other side of the bar. He moved hand over hand holding on to the edge of the bar. He paused and looked at the old till with 'National Cash Register' engraved on its front. He pressed down on the 'No Sale' button; the till went "Ding" and opened.

"It's full of old pennies," he said.

Crutch started to inspect the monies in the till. He held up four £1 pound notes, two 10-shilling notes, one white and one blue £5 note.

"All pre decimal," Shaky said.

"The Falcon collected antiques and vintage pornography," Crutch said.

"Jane Russell ain't pornographic," Walking Joe said.

"Was, almost, back then," Crutch said.

"When I was 13 I joined the St John Ambulance Brigade," Walking Joe said. "I joined so's I could go to the cinema twice a week and once on Sunday. I used to sit in the back row in a cadet's uniform. I used to look up at the light from the projector cut through dense cigarette smoke. I saw the power of Hollywood. I saw the dream factory. Jane Russell was there. Lana Turner, Humphrey Bogart. I saw *Citizen Kane*. And all you had to do was to pass a first aid exam given by Dr Zair and you entered into the industry of escapism for free."

"We used to buy one ticket and then go up to the emergency exit door beside the men's urinal," Crutch said, "one of us would press down the long bar opening the emergency door and then we would get in scot-free."

"I saw *Duck Soup* twice," Shaky said, "I hid under the seats in the front row after the Saturday matinee."

"I reckon we ought to lay Bill out flat," said Walking Joe.

"Yea, rigor sets in they'll never get him into the coffin," Shaky said.

"Leave him, the ambulance'll be here soon," Crutch said.

"What did you tell 'em?" Shaky asked.

"Told 'em that he'd collapsed," Crutch said.

"Massive coronary, that's what Bill had," Crutch said.

"He was dead when we got here," Shaky said.

"Drink up, lads 'cause after today the Falcon's nest will be locked, bolted, and barricaded," Walking Joe said.

"Yea," said Crutch, "Mrs Faulks, Edna, will come down on this lot like a ton of bricks."

"Wonder what will happen to the records," Shaky asked.

"Ox-fucking-fam because the generation of half-wits following us don't know how to listen to pure sound," Walking Joe said.

"The Falcon will go mad," Shaky said.

"When the Falcon lost his temper he'd clear a room with a hail of machine-gun spittle, cigar ash and used beer," Crutch said.

"Were you in the Wheatsheaf when he got barred for swearing?" Shaky asked.

"That time when he held up a copy of the *Advertiser*," Crutch said, "and he started mopping his head with that red handkerchief he always carried in his top pocket and he started cursing, his face all screwed up in disgust before he started to rant."

"About the hospital," Walking Joe said.

"Yes," Crutch said, "This is the saddest fucking story yet to appear in this fucking rag," he shouted and bits of his chewed cigar started shooting out of his mouth like shotgun pellets." "And I've paid national insurance contributions all my fucking life and they want to close the fucking hospital."

"And Ted never actually threw him out," Walking Joe said.

"Well," Crutch said, "he was six foot three and used to wrestle."

"And a great domino player," Joe said.

"Used to pull the cards out of a sack," Walking Joe said.

"Never shuffled them," Shaky said.

"Used a set of twelves," Crutch said.

"And twelves takes some working out," Shaky said.

"Always drank boilermakers in them days, a pint of mild and a Cutty Sark," Crutch said.

"What did he say before the start of every game?" Shaky asked.

"Gentlemen start your engines, let the game commence," the three friends shouted together as they raised their drinks in unison.

When the phone started to ring I was about to take the turning opposite Birds Barn where the A4110 splits away from the A4113.

Just up from the turning there is a layby. I pulled into it. Parked and waited for the hand free system to come alive.

"You have a call, do you have 'The Rugged' on?"

"Yes."

I assumed that it was on but since the lead from the car socket broke three weeks ago and had not yet been replaced, the contraption had to rely on the mains charge, anyway Dr Gutsell reached over to the rear seat and grabbed the device.

"Back to town," he said.

"What have we got?" I asked.

"A death."

"Where?"

"Tallow Fat Yard, the ambulance is there, a certain William Faulks."

"The Falcon, there is only one Bill Faulks."

"Unexpected."

"His father was a captain in one of Churchill's special behind the line forces."

"SAS?"

"No, before that, but a name with similar sounding letters, never actually joined the army but all the same was a major."

"Must of spoke French, fluently."

"He had the *Legion d'Honneur* from de Gaulle and a concession to import Champagne."

"Shall we go on to Knighton or turn back?"

"We go back, we release the ambulance."

"We'll go back."

I made a three-point turn.

I saw six rooks perched in the old oak tree above Birds Barn. And as I drove past Birds Barn I remembered a conversation I had with the owner in the Sun Inn when I asked why it was called Birds Barn.

"I dunna know," the farmer said, "There was a mon from the Heritage mob, nice enough fellow and he said that that barn was 450 years old. He could tell by the way the wooden beams was tied together with hazel pegs, that's what dates it," he said.

"It was where the tramps used to sleep, they used to make a bee line for it," he explained. "Just after the War there were tramps everywhere, ex servicemen, old soldiers, which proves how much the government thought about them that fought for the country. Anyway they used to ask for work like digging the garden or such like. Day labourers they were and they could turn their hand to anything. My mother would give them cups of tea."

And then I remembered the farmer screwing up his face whilst at the same time sticking his little finger in his right ear and turning it before extracting it and then looking at the remains of a nailful of wax before flicking it away.

"It must be a terrible thing to wake up clemmed and to have to do a day's work on an empty gut," he said.

And what he said and the way he said it could only have been said by someone who knows what a day's work is.

And as I drove back through his village past immaculate houses called the 'Old Bakery' and the 'Old Forge', I remembered when those houses were not immaculate, when real men baked bread and shod horses, when there were children playing in the street.

There was an ambulance in Tallow Fat Yard.

"What does the name mean?" asked my doctor.

"This is where they used to render the fat from cattle or sheep," I said.

"What for?" asked my doctor.

"Very important, candles, soap, oil for lubricating axles," I said.

"Of course, before oil was refined," my doctor said.

"Be prepared," I said.

"Why?" my doctor asked.

"Because I fixed the beer engine, I know what's inside," I said.

My doctor opened his door, lowered himself into the yard. His shoes crunched gravel as he moved and I heard the thoughtless chirping of sparrows and as my doctor walked past the ambulance, tomtits and chaffinches clashed for a few moments in violent skirmishes and then the birds scattered in all directions.

And I looked out of the windscreen and imagined a human soul being blown away by the breeze, erased, gone, evaporated and absorbed into a vast sunless dull cloud-filled sky.

16   Steinway

SPECIAL DAYS LIKE BANK HOLIDAYS are arranged within a time line like knots tied in a length of string.

This piece of string is called a year.

The Ancients used to light fires on the shortest day in order to encourage the sun.

It is one of the reasons we put lights on Christmas trees.

Two thousand years ago King Herod and the Romans got their knickers in a twist over the birth of a baby boy born in Bethlehem to a couple of Jews called Mary and Joseph of Arimathea.

Christmas Day.

Joseph was a carpenter. Jesus became his apprentice. He was time served.

A chippy was sent by God to save the world.

And that's only part of the story.

As I drove to work on the 2009th anniversary of the birth of the Son of God I realised that I had worked every Christmas Day for 15 years.

When I looked up at the moon still riding high in the sky, I saw that it was held inside a great dome by the cogs and wheels of a complicated mathematical equation.

Einstein was laughing.

A patient in the top ward was coughing.

As the night driver gave me the keys to the car he told me that there was hardly any fuel in it.

An indescribable, alarming wind blew along the corridor of the hospital.

"What?" I said, my nostrils anticipating the aroma of unknown possibilities.

"There's less than a quarter," he said.

"And no one filled it up," I said.

"Nothing open after six, they all closed early," he said.

"We are in the merde," I said.

Once upon a time there were 12 petrol stations open at any one time in our little town. Now there are two. Neither of them opens on Christmas Day. Once upon a time at least three of them had their owners living next to or somewhere near to the pumps, and what was more you knew who they were. You called them by their names.

"Mr Powell," "Mr Wontnor," "Mr Wilding," and you could go around to their house and you could knock them up and Mr Wilding would, if it was him you knocked up, look you up and down just to make sure who you were and he would ask you why the hell you wanted fuel at this time of night and you would probably say that you were doing something to the car and that you wanted to leave at four in the morning because you were going to Borth or somewhere else on the Welsh coast. And it was the truth because there was always something to be done to a car 40 years ago.

The points could go wrong or the carburettor was out and it would be good sense to grease the thing with a grease gun, every one had a grease gun, and Mr Wilding understood all those things and he would go to a little wooden shed and bring out a large handle which he would attach to the back of the petrol pump and he would turn it because it was a lot less trouble than opening up properly and switching the electric pumps on and you would have eight gallons at half a crown a gallon, which was a quid's worth, enough to get to Borth and back!

If however you happen to run out of fuel, through no fault of your own at this present time in our history, at the beginning of the 21st century, on our Lord's name day, his birthday, you are up shit creek without a paddle.

Fifty years ago you could count the number of cars in our town in your head and what's more you had to be fairly rich to afford one. Today it is not uncommon to see three vehicles parked directly on what was once the front lawn. But in spite of the abundance of horseless carriages, the lone garage proprietor who used to fill your car, wipe the windscreen, check the oil, whilst you sat in the car, that man is redundant, he is unable to make a living!

Do not attempt to crack the conundrum.

The calls started coming in.

There are many many reasons why people become ill during the festive season. More than likely the son or daughter, out of duty, makes the annual visit and finds the oldest member of the family in a shocking state of health, because for one reason or another the relative has gradually slipped into that time of human existence when the plumbing starts to malfunction.

Incontinence happens before the necessity of a Zimmer frame. Granddad has probably been almost pissing himself for a year, it's just that no one really noticed until the Christmas visit, which not only brings a couple of pairs of socks and a bottle of whisky but also guilt.

And so the calls started to come in on my last Christmas Day, but I did not know that it was going to be my last Christmas Day until two weeks later, when I became involuntarily trapped in a cavalcade of madness that started just as soon as the night driver handed me a car with hardly any fuel.

Calls appeared on the screen.

Time accelerated.

I told Dispatch.

I asked them where the nearest open filling station was.

They advised me to use Google.

Google is the brain. Google is the information. Google is knowledge. Google is the be all and the end all of our culture.

What did we do before Google?

I'll tell you what happened when we had a proper telephone system, when we had a real telephone exchange. What we did was to ring the operator and if it was Pam or Lesley, we would ask her what the number was for whoever we wanted and then Pam or Lesley would not only tell you the number, she would even ask you whether or not you wanted her to dial the number for you and connect you to the number!

Better than that, she would tell you what petrol station was open. Not only that but any one of the operators would ask you how you were because the system was operated by real humans who placed jack plugs into holes!

And that is the truth because for the last 20 years progress has been going backwards!

I Googled all the service stations in north Herefordshire and south Shropshire. The numbers came up. I dialled. No one answered. There is a Total petrol station 10 miles away. Google gave me the Total distribution centre in Milford Haven. No one answered the phone because it was Christmas day and half the population was nursing a hangover, opening presents or trying to put obese turkeys into ovens.

There were no filling stations open within a range of 30 miles.

Time accelerated.

I looked at the calls.

Gilbert Lenormand, Church Lane, Aston Moor. The name rang a bell.

There is only one Gilbert Lenormand.

Gilbert Lenormand is a philosopher in the kitchen with a degree from the Royal College of Music.

I opened the call.

Gilbert had fallen down the stairs.

There were three other calls, one in Presteigne and two in Knighton hospital.

My doctor was in the minor injuries unit with two nurses, and the gist of their conversation suddenly revealed the fact that one of the nurses had a husband who was the manager of a farm where there was a tank holding 2000 gallons of tractor diesel.

My doctor asked me whether or not our car would run on tractor diesel.

"Diesel is diesel," I said.

"I think it's red," the nurse said.

"I am not prejudiced," I said.

It was the solution to the problem. And because my doctor had been at one time in his career a surgeon, he was only too ready to agree. Surgeons, unlike general practitioners make instant decisions, they just do it. More than likely a GP will weigh it in the balance and think about it. It is the difference between the two beasts because, once the surgeon has pulled out his knife like a Gurkha; there is no going back!

We were on a mission, moving towards 2000 gallons of fuel.

Trout Hall stands in a Capability Brown landscaped park. It was the great man's last project.

Beyond the gate, we moved into the sweet air of that peculiar climate called wealth.

Trout Hall is a perfect house. We saw it from a distance. We drove to the rear of the great Georgian building, which was shaped like a horseshoe around a courtyard. It is where the stables are situated. And we saw horses being saddled by jockeys, for they were real racehorses and in training.

Forty-eight litres flowed into the tank by way of gravity for the tank was situated high enough to service the largest Combine Harvester.

"I will not accept payment," the manager said. And I looked at his hands holding the pistol at the end of the hose and his hands were those of a man who works the land.

"I'll make sure you get a bottle of Scotch," I said.

With the needle at last pointing to full and having

exceeded our expectations, we drove away from Trout Hall and with the tension of the morning ebbing away, I informed Dispatch what I had done even telling the dispatcher that the fuel was red.

It was a big mistake for one of the characteristics of a bureaucratic organisation is that it lacks any imagination or reason. It feeds on information that becomes a septic fermentation of excessive power and fear.

I drove slowly, like a horsedrawn carriage, raising my right hand now and again at imaginary people for I was moving through a park designed by Mr C. Brown.

There was a racetrack running parallel to the drive. I saw horses in the offside mirror. I watched six racehorses gaining. I cracked the window. The horses galloped past. The track turned away. My doctor saw it all and let me tell you that there is nothing like the sound of six galloping horses. It is no small wonder that right up until 1914 the cavalry was once the elite arm of any army.

We turned left. I yawned. My doctor stretched. We passed the cemetery. We passed a house whose owner was celebrating Christmas by nailing gigantic illuminated plastic sculptures onto the flank end of his house. There was nothing religious about the Post Impressionist carving of Santa Claus holding a whip over a red-nosed reindeer pulling a sleigh full of presents made in China by a race that will eat dog stew with chopsticks whilst worshipping a new Communist God called Mammon.

It is over 30 miles from our base to Aston Moor. The church is a Templar church, it is at the bottom of a large moor called the Bog which was drained during the last war. We arrived at 10.30

Gilbert Lenormand's house was number one. It was a large end of terrace Victorian building built in 1882 by a brickmaker.

My doctor knocked the door.

A woman whom I did not recognise opened it.

I sat in the car. I examined the building.

There were two altar candles in the bow window. There would be a Christmas tree inside the dining room. I wondered whether Gilbert still put real candles on his Christmas tree. If he did, there would be a red fire bucket full of sand next to the tree.

I sat in the car listening to the Third Programme.

Brahms *Sonata no 1*.

I saw a woman coming out of Ford Street, she was pushing a pushchair with six wheels. The complicated engineering involved in the design of the thing began to fascinate me. And then as the woman approached I saw that she was fat and what was more shocking was that she had an incredible beautiful face. Not only that but she was wearing what seemed to be a thin black mesh catsuit and the more I looked the more I saw because her underwear was visible.

She had to lean forward to push the pram.

Her udders were massive.

I wanted to tell her to fasten her coat.

She was larger than large.

Her body had disappeared into a mutation of obesity. She did not care. She had given up. Her body was redundant. She proliferated in all directions. In fact she was a woman who had completely absorbed herself into a sexless mutation and had disappeared.

She moved with great difficulty, hanging onto the complicated pushchair with one hand whilst texting someone with her other hand. It was an incredible sight. A human animal able to communicate with a member of the same species anywhere in the world by means of a small device held in the palm of her hand!

Thus Spake Zarathustra and I remembered the film *2001*.

But, and herein lieth the rub, it is now almost 2010 and the species who should inherit the Earth is now unable to run from a mad dog.

I looked at the dashboard as she passed just catching in the very peripherals of my vision her child under an eiderdown of Christmas presents.

I wondered where she was going.

Christmas dinner?

The pianist had arrived at the Andante.

I waited, thinking about food.

Over 40 years ago Gilbert Lenormand told me that mankind descended from trees. He told me that the human ape stopped living on fruits and started to slaughter animals. He told me that meals started after the slaughter because the butchering and sharing of meat brought the family together. He said that the first gatherings were confined to the very closest members of the ape family but that they eventually turned into feast days when close relatives and friends were included. He said that it was around the campfire where the elaboration of languages developed. From the crying of a baby, to a child shouting, "give me some".

We were having dinner at his house 40 years ago when he lived right on the border, in fact his kitchen was in Radnorshire and his dining room was in Shropshire. It was a celebration. We were celebrating the 10th anniversary of the Festival and Gilbert was a pianist. Gilbert was a cook. Some said a better cook than a pianist. Some said a better pianist than a cook.

It depended in which order you experienced it.

It was that time in the history of the Marches when Mike Oldfield heard the clarion in the church at Presteigne and then composed *Tubular Bells*.

Back then there was an abundance of niceness about. It was after the birth of Rock 'n Roll but before the birth of political correctness, before VAT, before hygiene certificates, before MRSA or any other kind of food poisoning or fear of smoking in public created by mad halfwits wearing yellow health and safety jackets, who would never have allowed the things we did in order to get a Festival on the road.

How did Gilbert fit into it all?

He was a pianist who gave his first public performance at the age of 11. Who came to England with his English mother to study at the Purcell School and the Royal College of Music. Who toured extensively in Spain, Italy and France before performing the Franz Lizst piano transcriptions of Beethoven's 5th and 6th Symphonies at Trout Hall as part of the second Festival season.

Gilbert stopped the audience dead.

Gilbert liked it here, he rented a house in order to compose music in the Marches.

But unlike Mr Oldfield, his compositions did not fit into the Virgin catalogue or any other catalogue. Musically he was 50 years ahead of his time.

So Gilbert became a cook.

What he did was to open his house by appointment only. No advertising, word of mouth, exclusive. And you were expected not to tell any one. It was the very opposite to marketing. In fact people used to fight to get into the place!

Each meal became a banquet, a one-off. You supplied the wine, which meant that you were expected to bring a good quality bottle to replace whatever Gilbert served and appropriate to the food he'd cooked, and if your bottle was plonk you had difficulty rebooking. The result was that his cellar became one of the best in the Marches.

All of us were part of 'The Dream'.

A Midsummer's Night Dream.

There were 10 of us.

We started with a salad, which was just a plain lettuce. This had been cut from the garden that very morning and was cleaned, gently dried and then dressed with a light oil and vinegar dressing whilst we were drinking an aperitif.

I saw Gilbert toss it in the kitchen.

He knew that if he had done it earlier then it would arrive at the table soggy.

I saw him take bottles of white wine from the refrigerator.

It was light, from Savoie. Grown at an altitude.

We were hungry and we were developing an appetite. This was due to the effects of the aperitif, which was being enhanced by the sipping of wine containing bubbles of sunshine and a common dressed lettuce.

In England lettuce is eaten with something else, a BLT, or it is placed on the side of a dish as decoration, it is never eaten on its own. It is never tasted, and if it is then it will be covered in salad cream, which is an English concoction designed to destroy the taste of anything that is put on or near it. The English do not know how to make a light oil and vinegar dressing. Salad dressings in Britain are only found in bottles with pictures of Paul Newman on the side and they are the next best thing to pure piss, in fact virgin's piss would taste better because it is very rare.

Next thing that happened was that three bottles of Chateauneuf Rosé were placed on the table. This is a light coppery bronze-coloured Rhone Valley wine ideal for drinking with fish.

A whole salmon had been cooked in Gilbert's Aga and, because Gilbert was French, it was a complete fish with its head intact.

After the first sip of wine every one started to enter into rapture. We were being transported to the pleasures of the table.

The salmon was served.

The wine had a delicate texture.

The leading actress had beautiful full breasts. I looked at each one in unison. My imagination was fired. Jokes were told.

The salmon melted in the mouth.

The wine had a delicate texture.

I looked at my wife.

I touched her leg.

The wine had a delicate texture.

I squeezed lemon onto the fish. I saw the skeleton of a fish on the table.

My brain was working overtime.

Each person cleaned his palate with more salad.

Four bottles of wine were finished.

And the bread had been freshly baked in the Aga.

It was as crisp as drumsticks.

The director of the play complimented Gilbert on the quality of his salad dressing.

Three bottles of *Les Michelons* Beaujolais arrived. It had of course been opened for some time. It was dense and serious. It was concentrated, red-fruited, and as a direct consequence of the first draught a warmth started to enter my limbs.

Lamb was served with a shallot sauce. It had been cooked to perfection. I had a ferocious appetite. I waited. Everyone ate the meat. There were no vegetables. We were eating in the style of the Dauphiné region of France where Gilbert came from, where each course is separate.

The lamb was red. So tender you could cut it with the back of a knife. The wine descending down my throat enhanced the meat.

The effect of eating caused our collective intellect to awaken.

Talking was initiated.

We talked about the last production and worried about the weather for the present production because it had been decided not to move it into the town hall, it was all too difficult and not worth it.

And we talked about other things and more things and also things in likewise.

French beans were brought to the table.

More bread was cut on a miniature guillotine.

I clearly heard the blade cut right through each piece.

The wine had structure; it had the ability to enhance my thoughts.

The *haricot verts* had been picked that morning. They had been steamed and then sautéed in garlic. The garlic had been grown in the garden.

It was not possible to get fresher ingredients.

And then a *Gratin Dauphinois* was placed on the table.

"Cuisine de la grandmère."

It could not get any better.

Not only that but a Bordeaux was placed on the table. A new order was initiated. This was the wine for the gratin. This was the wine for the potatoes that had been baked for two hours in full cream. This was the wine for the potatoes that had been planted and dug by Gilbert, and then cooked the same morning.

I worried about the small capacity of my stomach.

The gratin was perfectly seasoned. The Bordeaux had the slight taste of tannin, which came from the oak barrels it had once been stored in.

The bathroom, where I relieved myself, was equipped with a bidet. I had at that time in my life never seen one. I touched a tap and released somehow a fountain of water. I pondered the effect that such a device would have on a woman's nether regions.

I looked at my reflection in the mirror and realised that I should perhaps curtail the consumption of wine before my wife told me to do so. Unfortunately when I returned to the table an assortment of cheeses had been presented together with a couple of bottles of *La Chasse du Pape*. Now this a perfect wine for cheese, being almost 14 degrees.

Not only that but my friend Aubrey had already filled my glass so I had no alternative and there were also additional problems. There was a Shropshire blue from Cheshire. It was perfect and until you have eaten cheese with delicious fresh bread cooked on a wood-fired Aga, then you have never eaten cheese.

Full stop.

My legs felt strange.

My brain was becoming soft.

I was at that moment passing into a state of mind where it was impossible to tell appetite from hunger. I had started to indulge. Not only that but I was starting to monitor with my brain that operation called ingestion which begins when food enters the mouth and ends when it enters the oesophagus. Not only that but there was a strange tingling feeling entering my private parts which was leading to an uncontrolled erection. Now 40 years ago, erections were real and proper and could be almost painful. And could sometimes remain in position for a very long time.

It was the food.

The taste of the food was having a very strange effect. Not only that but I had to stop looking at the leading actress's breasts.

This was almost impossible since they were pendulous things.

By the time dessert had arrived the situation was under control. I had managed to move the erect member into an unrestrictive position.

Now the English buy more Champagne than any other tribe in the world. I have no idea why this is but the fact that they are willing to pay over a hundred pounds for a bottle of *William Deutz*, which is no more than a fizzy white wine with a name like a tractor, is more than interesting. Perhaps it is because there are now at this moment in time an abundance of gastro establishments in England serving 'lamb sweetmeats', a culinary euphemism for bollocks.

Back then Gilbert would have never dreamt that a chef in one of the best establishments in our little town could make a small fortune out of a parfait made out of olive oil and wild lime!

What Gilbert gave us was Williams pears soaked in red wine with a touch of brandy.

To clean the palate and to prepare the taste buds Gilbert opened two bottles of *Pétillant de Savoie*.

This is a white wine made by *méthode champenoise* in the high Savoie region of France most famous for sending chimney sweeps to Paris. The corks popped out in the correct manner. When the bubbles in the liquid spread over my tongue the numerous papillae on the surface of that organ started to react as they absorbed the substance. Not only that even my cheeks and nasal fossae recognised that it was a wine from that region where bubbles of sunlight can be captured in grapes and then released in a glass flute.

I thought that it was all over until a raspberry sorbet was placed in front of me. And then superb thick black coffee was provided. This was held down by a few doses of a medicinal liquid called Armagnac, imported from Gascony.

You would have thought that it was the end but no. What happened next was that Gilbert Lenormand appeared at the top of the stars wearing evening dress.

And you had no idea what you were about to receive.

And then Gilbert sat at his piano and he raised his hands in the air before he lowered them, just letting his palms hover for a second, just to get it straight in his mind, before he opened the gate of acoustical illusion because, what Franz Lizst did to Beethoven's *Pastoral* was to liberate from the orchestra all the sharp diamond syncopated piano notes.

And Gilbert made all those notes fly into the air like night moths dancing around altar candles.

When Gilbert had finished playing it took more than 30 seconds for the echoes to fall and scatter like autumn leaves across the floor.

And as he got up from his piano and walked into his kitchen we felt a gentle breeze from all the used empty notes.

And we applauded.

And Gilbert came out of his kitchen holding a large coffee pot.

And he lowered his head and he smiled.

And it was something you never ever forgot.

When my doctor came out of the house, he walked towards the car, opened the back door and threw his bag onto the rear seat.

"He's going in, I need an admittance letter," he said.

I followed my doctor back into the house.

I had to speak to the woman.

I had to find out if he'd had *réveillon*.

"Yes there were four of us," she said.

"Good," I said.

"We had it last night with friends," she said.

"Good," I said.

When my doctor had finally finished and the ambulance had arrived, as he was buckling his seat belt, he asked me what I was talking to Gilbert's wife about.

"Food," I said.

"Christmas dinner?" my doctor asked.

"The French call it *réveillon*," I said.

"They eat it the night before," my doctor said.

"They did last night with friends," I said.

My doctor reached for the Rugged laptop.

He hit the keyboard and then he paused.

"There was a grand piano in the front room," my doctor said.

"Model D, serial number 508255," I said.

17   The Cherry Tree

I WOKE AND FOUND MY ROOM enveloped in brightness.

Six o'clock and the morning was already glaring with early sunshine.

At that solemn hour I heard a hacking cough and the footsteps of a nurse moving along the ward above my head. I guessed that she was going towards the patient who was crying out "NURSE, NURSE, NURSE," for a hospital ward is never filled with the harmonious breathing of sleeping people.

I turned towards the TV screen whilst my right hand searched for the clicker.

BBC 24 Hour News:

"And there is nothing left except the silent majority which is nothing more than a statistical beacon placed at the horizon of a disappeared social order whose representation is no longer possible."

What on earth was the idiot with the small pony tail talking about?

For some reason or other the muscles in my calf started sending electrochemical signals right into my brain telling me that I had cramp and for a few moments I decided that the cramp was caused by the idiot on the box who was declaring that the masses did not care.

I moved my leg.

After a few minutes the cramp disappeared and the weather forecast began with a giant map of the UK covered in all the different signs like isobars and clouds and the presenter became animated and talked about a circumpolar high pressure region and I became fascinated by the weather forecast until the phone started to ring and I cursed as my feet got caught up in the end of my sleeping bag.

We had less than one hour before our shift finished and now we had a call in Church Stretton.

I hit the keyboard.

The computer screen came alive.

There was only one call on the screen for Church Stretton. It was in fact Cardington, near Church Stretton and I just could not believe that a patient with thrush needed a home visit.

Nor could my doctor after I had rattled his door before opening it a little, just enough to push my arm through and drop the call sheet onto his cot.

"How on earth can thrush be an urgent call?" he shouted.

I did not know the answer, all I was concerned about was that we should finish at seven but won't because someone has a problem with her nether regions.

"Let me have a look at the screen," my doctor said standing in his shorts and stocking feet.

"There it is," I said pointing to the call. And there it was.

"This is not real," my doctor said.

"Of course we could be taking part in a virtual reality show, we could just walk out of here into a void," I said.

My doctor shook his head.

"What we will do is this," he said, "I will do this call on the way home and I will fax the call sheet back to base when I get to work."

"You are working this morning then," I said.

"This afternoon," he said, "the trouble is that I have forgotten my mobile."

"Then we both have to go," I said.

"Why?" he said.

"Because I am not letting you out of my sight without a means of communication," I said.

"There is a solution to the problem," he said.

"Like what?" I said.

"Like my wife starts work at six," he said.

"What difference does that make?" I said.

"She manages Sunny Bank nursing home," he said.

"So," I said.

"She brings our son in with her when I work nights and I take him back with me directly to his school, what I'll do is to use his mobile, I will give you his number," he said.

I nodded. It was a solution to the problem because if he came back here he would be late. And if he came back here so would his son be late and I also would be late.

"So what you are going to do is to pick up your boy at Sunny Bank and take him to the call and then take him to school," I said.

"Affirmative," my doctor said.

I nodded. The doctor went back into his room. He came back dressed. He was carrying his bag. His stethoscope was around his neck. It was ten past six.

"You'll want to take a box of Trimethoprim," I said.

"Good thinking," he said.

I removed a packet from the drug cabinet. My doctor put it in his pocket. He walked out. He pulled the door shut. The doctor's car pulled out from the car park. I closed the drug cabinet. I locked it. I made coffee. I phoned Dispatch.

The dispatcher logged the departure time.

"What was that call number again?" she said.

I told her.

There was a long pause.

"It is not the correct number," the dispatcher said.

"WHAT," I said.

"I think that the doctor's gone to the wrong call," the dispatcher said.

"WHAT," I said.

"Look at the screen," the dispatcher said.

I looked at the screen.

Now there were two calls on the screen, one for Cardington,

which was not even a visit, and one for Cardingmill Valley, which was urgent.

Both had Church Stretton post codes.

The real call had been trapped in the ether or the dispatcher had taken her time to press the send button. Not only that but the real call really was urgent, chest pains, short of breath.

Shit was happening.

I rang the number the doctor had given me. Which was his boy's phone. There was a message from Orange telling me that the phone number was unavailable.

Shit was falling and it was twenty past six.

I had to print the correct call. I had to find my doctor; I had to catch him up. The printer jammed. I cursed. I used words that had not yet been invented.

The doctor now had a 15 minutes head start.

I ran through the door. I had to get to the nursing home A.S.P It was the only way.

I arrived at the nursing home at half past six.

His car was not in the car park.

He must have gone.

Shit was falling.

I found his wife. I explained. I had to check the boy's mobile number. The stupid wife had it on her mobile phone. It was in her handbag. She had not quite grasped what was going on. She took her time and decided to start a conversation with a nurse about the state of some old codger on the edge of extinction. I had the urge to shake her. In fact I moved towards her with that action in mind as she manipulated her phone with her thumb.

She finally looked directly at me. We compared numbers. They were the same.

I dialled the number. I got the orange voice again.

Why had the phone not been turned on?

Why didn't my doctor make sure that his son's phone was switched on?

I was sailing into the biggest cock-up on planet earth.

It was twenty-five to seven when I left four sets of rubber prints on the tarmac. And what was more it was Wednesday, which was the day they collected the rubbish and the bastards were there with their truck all decorated with orange lights revolving, pulsating and they were running about in all directions wearing yellow jackets.

I had to mount the pavement narrowly missing a yellow jacket who was pulling a black bin; he waved his fist at me.

Gimme all your hate!

Jesus H Christ and I left the town doing 85.

The doctor had a 20 minutes start. I had to get there. He would take his time. He would not drive as fast as me. He would follow Tom-Tom I was following my brain. I was going over the edge.

Wenlock Edge.

It was the most direct way but and it was a big dangerous but, because all the roads over The Edge are single lanes.

There is nowhere in the world as dangerous as a single lane road. Nowhere, especially in England where we have hedges and you can't see around corners because of the high hedges, all conserved by conservation officers sitting in conservation offices scratching their backsides. Nobody thinking about the school run and it was now the hour. That hour, which is the very beginning of the school run because even if you are only doing 40 and a 4x4 comes in the opposite direction containing a family on the school run, also doing 40, you are looking at a brick wall at 80.

I was at times hitting 70.

Go slower ... all the time expecting a countrywoman to come at me driving one-handed with a mobile phone in her ear, because she's making a rendezvous with another Barbour-dressed female driving in the same manner. Not only that but any female will turn and look at her child fidgeting on the back seat, not realising that the thing is hyper because of the E numbers in the cereals which will have, by the time she reaches a blind corner, just about started to mix with the digestive enzymes in the little bastard's pancreas.

Death at dawn and it will be my fault!

Go slower.

My hands were sweating.

It was turning into one of those times when you feel as if you have lost control. That anything can happen and if it does it will be your fault because you have not thought it through, because you should never let a doctor out of your sight certainly not unless he's got a mobile.

And now I was in the process of riding a giant roller-coaster in deep concentration, totally immersed in the road ahead coming up to sharp corners, driving almost by instinct, sure that I knew the way. Zig-zagging past potholes, clipping the verge, foredoomed and frightened that something would come the other way.

Go slower ... but I couldn't.

I felt like Icarus flying on his own wings borne to destruction.

When I arrived at the exact location. The doctor was not there.

After hesitating for a few moments I decided to turn.

As I reversed into a drive his car came round the corner.

I had made it.

Nothing more mattered.

It could and would be sorted.

I took my time getting back.

I emptied my bladder on the top of Wenlock Edge. It was marvellous. I zipped whilst at the same time listening to the morning and I was tired.

Weary.

Thankful.

The Gods had been with me. I had pushed my luck. It was over. All I had to do was to drive slowly and listen to the news.

The cleaners were there when I got back. I had not locked

the room. The bed was still assembled. My sleeping bag was on the floor.

I took my time.

Firstly I made coffee.

Then I thought about where I was.

I was in the workhouse.

Our hospital is built on the site of the old workhouse. And for a moment I remembered that my grandmother would not go into this hospital, instead she died at home because for her it was a place designed to make life as unattractive as possible.

It was a place for the undeserving poor.

"It should be like a cold bath," said Edwin Chadwick, who was a civil servant in 1850 in charge of it all, "it should be unpleasant in contemplation but invigorating in its effect," he said.

I have a large portrait of my grandmother in a beautiful hardwood frame.

A journeyman artist did it.

My grandmother was right.

I was in the workhouse.

Two hours later at home, I had just finished a late breakfast, in fact I was holding a cup of Italian coffee made the old fashioned Italian way in the correct device when the phone rang.

It was our operations manager.

"Would you hang up and I will ring you back?" he said.

"Why?" I said, thinking it was about what had happened earlier.

"We want to amplify and record the conversation," he said.

I put the phone down and as I waited for the phone to ring I tried to recall everything that had happened over the last four hours.

Nothing and everything.

I went over the racecourse at almost a ton but there was only a tractor cutting grass on the golf course.

Nothing happened. I was the only car on the country lanes. I never had a near miss.

The phone rang. I paused. I lifted the receiver.

There was an echo in the phone. I started to worry, what did he want? What had happened? What is so important that it should be recorded and amplified?

I tend to forget things that have happened recently like where did I put my glasses or what was I doing a few moments ago.

Had something happened that I was unaware of?

I pressed the receiver to my best ear. More than one idiot was listening. It was going to be an inquisition. I wondered what the hell had gone wrong.

"Right," the operations manager said, "how much red diesel did you put in the car a fortnight ago on Christmas day?"

I was not prepared for the question.

"How much illegal fuel did you put in the car?" he repeated, and he was getting excited.

"I have no idea," I said, half relieved that it was nothing serious.

"You must have some idea," he said, and he was even more excited.

"A tank full," I said.

"How much is that?" he said and now he was really getting wound up.

And then all of a sudden it came to me. This was the crash I had been waiting for. I was hitting it head on. I was hitting a brick wall in slow motion at well over 80. This was what I thought was going to happen at a quarter to eight this morning.

This was what had made my hands sweat.

Fate gives with one hand and takes away with the other.

And I realised that the bastards had no idea what had happened a few hours ago. They had no idea that I had charged around like a mad man!

I pushed the earpiece of the phone right into my ear.

They were talking amongst themselves.

The nest of bureaucrats had taken two whole weeks to come out of the woodwork like fat white wriggling grubs.

"He won't answer," pause, "Check the transcript."

"Hello," he said.

"A cold bath full," I said thinking about Edwin Chadwick.

"Well how much is that?" the operations manager asked.

"I have not got a fucking clue," I said, thinking about Christmas day and Gilbert on the stretcher going into the ambulance whilst at the same time recalling Housman's poem about the cherry tree.

Now of my three score years and ten

Twenty will not come again

And take from seventy springs a score

It only leaves me fifty more.

And I thought about the 15 Christmas Days I'd worked and if I only live for three score and ten then only two will come again.

And nobody was talking. All the words had run out. They were in a state of shock. I was turning the tables.

It is surprising what an old Anglo Saxon word can do.

"Because I am 68," I said.

"I beg your pardon, you do realise that this call is being recorded and that what you did and just said could lead to your dismissal," the man said.

And I sucked his words like a chocolate liqueur until the centre inside dissolved like alcohol on my tongue, infusing my brain and everything became realer than real and clearer than clear.

"You are acting like an inquisitor," I said.

And there was no response. Just a silence but they were talking, whispering. My job was going from plus to minus. I was hurting my good ear because I was pressing the earpiece right into my ear trying to hear how many of them were listening at one and the same time. And as I stood holding he phone to my ear I suddenly thought, shall I jump or wait for the push? Because I sensed that there was some kind of trap forming, that the thoughts in that room on the other end of the line were fermenting in a way that makes manure seem sweet.

"We are trying to get to the bottom of what happened on Christmas day," he said.

"The car was empty, " I said.

"Why didn't you bring it to Shrewsbury?" he said.

"I was fucking empty," I said.

And somebody was suggesting that the questioner should ask another question and I could not quite hear what he or she was saying because all the conversation in that room was decomposing and fermenting into whispers.

"It was a quarter full," he said.

"I do not like inquisitions on the telephone," I said.

"We are trying to get to the bottom of it," he said.

"Make an appointment, eyeball to eyeball," I said.

"This is serious," he said.

"Bollocks," I said, putting the phone down.

I had decided to jump.

And I remembered my mother-in-law who used to walk into a café at eight am every morning in the main square of Grenoble, France, and order a coffee and a cognac and she used to drink the coffee and then pour the cognac into the warm cup and so I finished my coffee and I added a cognac to my warm cup, a good dose, a correct dose and I slowly drank it and it was very good and I felt a Charlie fall off my back.

Sometimes success is buried in the garden of failure.

Also by Mike Sargent

My Old Man the Gasman

YOUNG MIKE SARGENT'S FATHER, JACK, yearned to be a standup comic but his family refused to allow it. He became a gas fitter instead. This is the story of the unwilling gasman's career and the adventures of his young son during and after the war. By turns bawdy, sad, often hilarious, crammed with unforgettable characters and brilliant narrative, it is marvellously entertaining.

You don't have to live in South Shropshire and its environs, or in Ludlow, as I do, to enjoy this remarkable account, because it could well apply to any rural town in the immediate aftermath of WWII. However, if you are so privileged, to learn of what we have lost in the past 60 years is likely to bring tears to the eyes of sadness for the passing of a simpler and more engaging way of life as well as of laughter. Much of the humour arises naturally, organically in fact, from the characters and their interaction with each other and the landscape in which they live, love, and endure. And it arises as simply through the curious eyes of a boy as he grows from ten years to fourteen. So in some ways this is a coming of age story, which goes to show that lads who grow up in the old rural muck of the farmyard get to know a lot about sex before reaching the age at which they can understand it.

The evocation of the delightful region of South Shropshire's landmarks will delight in the telling, but perhaps one warning to the inhabitants of nearby Craven Arms, which is briefly described as being like Borth without the sea, 'nothing'.

Roger M Kean in goodreads.com

First published in 1998, it is now available in a Kindle edition from Amazon.

Acknowledgements

WITH THANKS TO MY WIFE, ROSELYNE, without whose help nothing would make sense. Also to Mark Brett, who told me that I could really write, and my publisher, David Burnett.

Not forgetting all the doctors and drivers at Shropdoc for their help and encouragement.